Praise for *The Earth-Sheltered Greenhouse Book*

"I have fallen in love with this book because it is the answer to most of my greenhouse problems. I was concerned about building an above ground greenhouse due to the fact that I would have to run electricity to the building to heat/cool it. The earth berm concept is so painfully smart am left wondering why more people don't practice this? This book also solved my problem of a location for vermiculture and where to house the chickens I am soon to get for the winter. In order to get a better handle on construction methods I also bought the author's other book ($50.00 and up undgerground house) but if you are a little familiar with construction you'll do fine with this one. A must buy right now due to the need for sustainable living!!!!!!!!!!!!!!!!"
Lana Lambert, *Amazon 5-Star Review*

"An interesting, quite complete and entertaining book. The author gives the reader the benefit of many years of trial and error and some well-presented design elements that are not well treated in many other greenhouse books .... He got into greenhouse design choices and did a very nice job .... I liked the book. It was a pleasant read and the pearls of wisdom .... keep up the readers interest."
Tom Karasek, *Hobby Greenhouse*

"This design is so unique and so efficient, this is phenomenal .... an amazing greenhouse system"
Jane Nugent, *Jane Nugent's Garden Talk, WPTT Radio – TV, Allison Park (Pittsburg) PA*

"For more than three decades, Oehler has built a series of underground dwellings experimenting with low-cost, earth-insulated housing at his 46-acre homestead near Bonners Ferry. He has turned his hobby into an industry, producing first a book ("The $50 and Up Underground House Book") and then videos and more house-making manuals. Now he's produced his latest: "The Earth-Sheltered Solar Greenhouse Book." .... With this kind of practical experience and success, he's become an international expert on owner-built housing. His jolly, full bearded visage has been seen on television interviews around Europe and across the U.S. He even finds a place at academic forums. .... He includes enough drawings and photos for anyone to duplicate his designs .... If you want a greenhouse and you want to build it yourself, a good place to start is by visiting with Mike Oehler."
Bill London, *Lewiston Tribune*

"Detailed instruction on how to design and build an earth-sheltered greenhouse. .... Should be of interest to gardeners intent on raising as much of their own food as possible. Since I'm not planning to build any kind of greenhouse, I started out intending to just skim the book so I could tell you about it. But it was so entertaining I read everything except the technical parts."
Sue Lowe, *Garden Editor, South Bend Tribune*

In many North-American climates, the benefit of a greenhouse is apparent, especially to those who rely on an extended growing season to provide veggies and herbs to carry through the winter months. Mike Oehler, author of the pioneering work "The $50 and Up Underground House Book" has been gardening---and feeding himself--- from his hand-built earth-sheltered greenhouse for more than 30 years and has now released "The Earth-Sheltered Solar Greenhouse Book" a title dedicated to the subject of a sustainable, eco-sensitive, solar-heated grow house that just about anyone can build for a fraction of the cost of a conventional greenhouse structure.

The 220-page soft cover is a combination gardening guide, construction handbook, and life-experience manual, all filtered through Oehler's singular philosophy, which is as practical as it is unconventional. The author's aim is to advocate affordability and self-reliance through the application of simplicity, which he's certainly done with this project. The book covers the theory, design, and construction of the greenhouse (using Mike's low-cost PSP ---post, shoring, polyethylene--- technique): glazing, insulation and ventilation; beneficial critters and those that aren't so; solar energy input: the cold sink system; earth-tempering; and thoughts on how to use the completed structure. .... keep in mind that this greenhouse functions with no heat input in northern Idaho and carries hardier varieties through the winter.

Back Home Magazine

"Every winter, gardeners dream of owning a greenhouse—a warm and sometimes sunny place to tend plants and overwinter tropical favorites. If high heating bills have kept you from realizing that dream, this may be the book that inspires you to dig right in.

The author lives in an earth-sheltered home and grows his own veggies in a working greenhouse that is heated by the sun. In chapters about glazing, insulation, heat tubes and pest management, you'll learn the basics of a solar-powered greenhouse and be treated to plans, photos and random notes about the process, including the use of rabbits as part of the growing cycle. The solar heat idea will work best if you have a hillside and sunny location, but you can harness the sun anyplace there is light and soil.

The author also wrote "The $50 & Up Underground House Book" and his home has been featured on HGTV and in various magazines. Even if you never intend to grow a thing, the book is a fascinating look into the mind of a modern day rebel."

Marianne Binetti, *Seattle Post Intelligencer*

"With food prices being so high, many gardeners are considering growing edibles in greenhouses. This need not cost a fortune, especially if you go solar. I highly recommend "The Earth-Sheltered Solar Greenhouse Book -- How to Build an Energy Free Year-Round Greenhouse" by Mike Oehler.

Using Oehler's recommendations, anyone can afford a four-season greenhouse. This is illustrated with photos and sketches and complete, step-by-step instructions.

Through trial and error, the author discovered a way he could extend the growing season. His revolutionary construction method costs a fraction of the conventional approach. Furthermore, you can use salvaged materials that others are throwing away. With the authors system, the energy costs for the greenhouse is minimal. The automatic vent requires no energy. You also have the option of adding a root cellar and including animals such as rabbits or poultry to your greenhouse. This book is perfect for organic gardeners as the author emphasizes organic methods."

Connie Krochmal, *Landscaping Editor, Bella Online*

"While it is true the timing of the appearance of this book couldn't be better with regard to the recently skyrocketing prices of energy, food and building materials (since it shows how gardeners can save considerable money on all three), the ideas in it haven't sprung up overnight -- rather, the author has worked them out over three decades, long enough to determine their long-term viability. Mike Oehler's specialty is figuring out how to thrive with minimal cash outlay; actually, it's more than just figuring out; it's actually doing it! This book resulted from Oehler's need for an inexpensive greenhouse to extend the quite short growing season in northern Idaho. ... For those who don't want to build a full-blown greenhouse, there are abundant suggestions applicable to cold frames and even temporary row covers, including advice on choosing glazing materials and insulation, dealing with pests, (such as carpenter ants, which Oehler routs by blowing cayenne pepper into the ants tunnels every few days), and managing microclimates. There is also an interesting chapter on adding (small) livestock like rabbits to greenhouses. And there is another chapter about designing root cellars (and also about a root cellar designed by gophers!). For the truly ambitious, Oehler even introduces the (again, dirt-cheap; pun intended) "garden house" that combines living quarters with an attached solar greenhouse.

The most technical chapters are toward the back of the book, giving quite complete information on seasonal sun angles at different locations in the U.S., with a view toward managing greenhouse microclimate year-round; construction engineering specifications; detailed cross-sectional and plan views of small and large solar greenhouses built with the P/S/P technique and bills of materials for simple greenhouses.

This book combines practical advice with entertaining anecdotes to provide one of the best presentations we've seen of the results of homegrown horticulturally related research.

Greg and Pat Williams *Hortideas*

CRITICAL ACCLAIM FOR MIKE OEHLER'S THE $50 AND UP UNDERGROUND HOUSE BOOK

"... he has written a wonderfully unsophisticated manual and filled it with design ideas and even plans for building in different ways and on different kinds of terrain...impressive...entertaining, sometimes philosophical...a valuable document.
"**Daniel Lusk, *National Public Radio***

If you're thinking of building your own livable, pleasant light and airy and tuned-into-nature home, this book is for you."
The Mother Earth News

"By far the best example of low-cost earth sheltering we've found"
Earth Shelter Living Magazine

"This guy literally wrote the book on subterranean housing and sold more than (105,000) copies of *The $50 & Up Underground House Book.* He lives in his own creation. It's a little snug but it's custom-built and has all the creature comforts. You can barely see it, a dream getaway nestled deep in the mountains of scenic Northern Idaho on 40 acres of land. Imagine, it, all yours for $500. That's what subterranean pioneer Mike Oehler created when he...built one of the nations first underground houses in 1971...Today his little house in a hillside is a rustic gem...It's like having an underground log cabin...and somehow, eight feet underground, there's still lots of light here."
HGTV, *The Subterraneans*

"It's obvious Oehler's onto something." **-- *The Chicago Sun Times***

THE FOOD YOU ARE EATING TODAY IS HAZARDOUS TO YOUR HEALTH.

You have long known your food is laced with pesticides, herbicides, fungicides, waxes, hormones, preservatives, artificial coloring and flavoring. You probably realize produce can lose half its vitamin content during transportation and sitting on market shelves. You may have learned that as much as 60% of the food sold in the supermarkets today is genetically modified and that much of it is irradiated. Now we know much of it is filthy, too, tainted with harmful bacteria. Our spinach, our green onions, our lettuce — none of the supermarket produce today can be considered safe. According to the *New York Times*, every year 76 million Americans get sick and 325,000 are hospitalized — because of tainted food. Some die from it.

Is there a way to guarantee your food is absolutely fresh, pure, organically grown in healthy soil and free of E. coli and other biological contaminants? Yes there is! Grow and harvest it yourself year-round in a free-energy, earth-sheltered solar greenhouse. Electricity goes out? Energy prices soar? It doesn't matter. The greenhouses described in this book can take your plants through bitter cold nights and long winters with just the direct energy of the sun and what is stored in the earth. Here Mike Oehler, author of *The $50 & Up Underground House Book*, shows you how to design and build an earth-sheltered solar greenhouse for pennies on the dollar — the definitive book on energy efficient greenhouses.

The Earth-Sheltered Solar Greenhouse Book

How to build an energy free year-round greenhouse

by Mike Oehler

Illustrated by:
Ross
Anita Bedard
Katie Purviance
Cassie Eisenhower
Chandel Oyharsabal
Sarah Tye
David Fairall

© 2007 by Mike Oehler

Library of Congress Control Number: 2006940268

ISBN 9780960446407

All rights reserved. No part of this work covered by the copyright hereon may be reproduced or used in any form or by any means — graphic, electronic, or mechanical, including photocopying, recording, taping, or information storage and retrieval systems — without written permission of the publisher.

Printed in the United States of America by
United Graphics

5 7 9 10 8 6 4

Published by Mole Publishing Company
Bonners Ferry, Idaho

Readers are invited to use the design or construction methods and features described in this book. For permission to build from any specific plans, please contact:

Mike Oehler
333 Gandhi Way
Bonners Ferry, Idaho 83805
www.undergroundhousing.com

Please include an SASE (self-addressed, stamped envelope) with all mail correspondence if you wish a written reply.

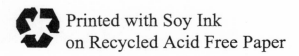 Printed with Soy Ink
on Recycled Acid Free Paper

Other works by the author

Books:
      The $50 & Up Underground House Book
      One Mexican Sunday
      The Hippy Survival Guide to Y2K

DVD's:
      The Underground House Workshop and
        Survival Shelter Seminar— three DVD set
      (Construction, Design, Shelter)

VHS:
      The Battle of Seattle
      The WTO protests through the lens of a
        protestor

CD
      Out of the Woods
      Original and traditional folk songs

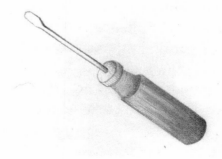

ACKNOWLEDGMENTS

Many people helped to bring this book to completion. In Idaho Vern Wilson of Bonners Ferry Glass and Jessica Berube of Northern Home Center have gracefully given of their time to answer questions, as have organic growers Marsha Semar and Kathi O'Leary. Mark Lathrom, AIA, in Post Falls, Idaho, helped conceptualize many of the early sketches. Architectural puzzles have been handled with expertise by Chris Royer, AIA, one of Massachusetts leading "green architects" and one of my best friends. Another great friend is Rob Roy who interrupted writing of his 13th book to read and proof this manuscript and write the forward. He is a legend in his time and an inspiration to countless people who struggle towards affordable housing. Tony Tiverious, my great brother-in-law, has come out of retirement as a top Chicago structural engineer to give us the load and stress tables in this book as he did on my underground house book back in the 1970's.

Then there are Jill and David Fairall who with their wonderful children, Ian and Hannah, share my land. Despite home schooling the children and keeping her household in order Jill graciously shares evening meals, helps on dishwashing and running the company, saving this author several hours a day for writing. If that isn't enough, she has proofread this manuscript multiple times, given valuable advice, and did the indexing.

David Fairall has turned out to be a wonder on the computer in not only typing the manuscript but in learning the software to help lay out the book. Our collaboration has been both rewarding and deeply satisfying. He is a diligent researcher. An expert photographer, he took the photos and did the captions on page 169 and 232. He turned into an astonishing artist in touching up many drawings and doing all the structural renderings from page 176 on . The computer did the renderings? No more than a paintbrush does the painting. David's a computer artist.

A number of other drawings in this book had two or more artists besides computer enhancement. Three of the artists did not sign their work so we aren't entirely sure of the specific artist or artists for each drawing. However, we are sure that Ross, who set the tone and was the artist to emulate, drew the hammer on page 42 and the strawberries on page 82. Anita Bedard, despite health problems, did many of the plant and vegetable drawings. Examples of her fine work are on pages 26 and 148. Katie Purviance, a U of Idaho architecture student who dropped out and disappeared into the cab of an over–the-road semi in the midst of her job with us, did all the insects in chapter 11, most of the earlier structural renderings and the drawings on page 53.

Then there were three astonishing Idaho art students at Bonners Ferry High School who cranked out numerous professional quality drawings for us. Senior Cassie Eisenhower, described by her art teacher as "the most talented art student I've ever had" did the drawings, among others, on pages 13 and 87. Sophomore Chandel Oyharsabal, grand champion artist at the Boundary County Fair, has examples of her fine drawings on pages 134 and 161, while Sophomore Sarah Tye, First Place fair winner, displays samples of her excellent work on pages 149 and 151.

Grudgingly Dedicated to

The Gophers of America

honorable adversaries

TABLE OF CONTENTS

Foreword by Rob Roy
A Cautionary Introduction

Chapter

Page

1 Prologue to A Happy Discovery 17
2 The Grow-hole Concept 21
3 The Grow-hole in Practice 27
4 The First Cold-Sink Greenhouse 33
5 P/S/P Construction 43
6 Glazing 57
7 Insulation 71
8 Ventilation 79
9 Passive Solar Energy Collection 83
10 Heat Tubes 89
11 Bugs and Other Pests in Your Greenhouse 93
12 Rabbits and Other Beneficial Critters 111
13 Growing Tips 127
14 Root Cellars 135
15 The Garden House 149
   Photos 164-169
16 Designing Your Own Greenhouse 171
17 Building Plans and Costs 199
18 Random Notes 211
19 A Final Word About Gophers 215

   Index 218
   Bibliography 222
   Resources 224

Foreword

by Rob Roy

The Earth-Sheltered Solar Greenhouse Book. The book's title itself is very nearly its own foreword. Listen:

"Earth-Sheltered." Our mutual friend, Mac Wells, would shelter almost *everything* with earth: bridges, birdhouses, even airports. But greenhouses make particular sense, as you'll soon learn. I've been earth sheltering my houses almost as long as Mike has – he has the advantage of having been born eight years earlier – and for many of the same reasons described in his *$50 and Up Underground House Book* and this current work: aesthetics, comfort, and various kinds of protection.

Plants particularly need protection. They don't do well when they freeze. Like friend Mike, Jaki and I live in a cold climate, not far from Montreal, one of the coldest cities in the world. While our above-ground growing season is not quite as short as his, it *is* short. We, too, have found that we can harvest greens through the winter in our greenhouse. While not directly earth-sheltered, it is attached along its long north side to our earth-sheltered house, which is always toasty and warm, and so we gain the same advantage: a temperate climate. An earth-sheltered greenhouse can be put where you want: near the home, near the garden, whatever. The net effect of earth-sheltering for people near the Canadian border is, effectively, like moving the structure 1000 miles further south. But earth-sheltering is an advantage *anywhere*, because of the tempering influence of earth's thermal mass.

"Solar." Plants gotta have it. Conventional, all-glass, above-ground greenhouses get plenty of solar, but their temperature swings range from Venusian to Plutonian. Earth-sheltered greenhouses have solar gain, too, but they budget out the sun's heat both on a daily and on a long-term basis. Mike does the numbers for us in Chapters 3 and 4.

"Greenhouse." Why bother? Isn't this a lot of work for little gain? Not if you do it right, as described herein. Greenhouses (1) extend the growing season by providing a place to start plants a month or more before the last frost-free date, (2) enable the owners to harvest fresh vegetables through the long winter, (3) expand the *variety* of fruits and vegetables that you can grown in colder climes, and (4) provide a piece of intoxicating tropical space on your normally winter-frigid homestead, saving round-trip air to Bora Bora.

"Book." Yep, it tells you how, and in Mike's colloquial, humorous, sometimes curmudgeonly and always inimitable manner. I've always prided myself on sharing information on low-cost green building techniques in my books, but Mike outflanks me every which way from a Mexican Sunday: the guy builds cheap, *dirt* cheap, and I say this with begrudging admiration. After too long a remission, the happy hippie hobbit surfaces once again to improve the nick of time.

Rob Roy is the author of *Earth-Sheltered Houses: How to Build an Affordable Underground Home* and Director of Earthwood Building School inWest Chazy, New York.

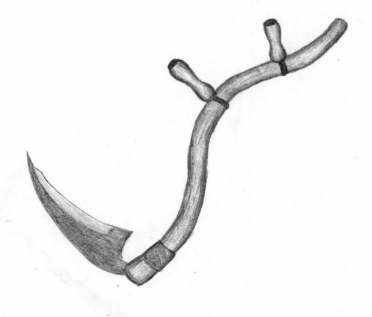

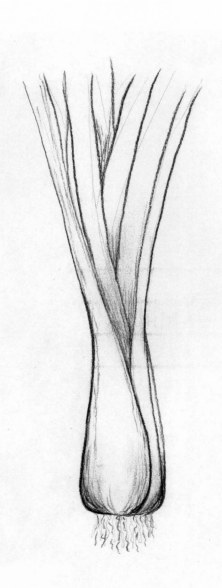

A Cautionary Introduction

What we are going to teach you in this book is how to put together a greenhouse that is not only wonderfully inexpensive to build, but that in many cases will cost nothing to heat – you will capture the sun's energy, and utilize that which is stored in the earth. For most of the people of North America this should mean at least an eight-month growing season and a twelve-month harvest. This is a significant step forward. It will save you many dollars and much effort whether you are a professional grower, hobby gardener or homestead sustenance grower. It can give you glorious organic food, and it will help break you free of corporate control.

I look at the agribusiness professionals of today with dismay and alarm. The harm agribusiness is doing to the soils, ground water, atmosphere, foods, animals and peoples of, first the USA, and now the rest of the world, has been well documented. Less well understood is the degradation it has brought to the cultures of those in the industrialized nations. And almost unrecognized, in the U.S. at least, is the fact that the corporations, wielding the power of controlled legislatures and administrations, the International Monetary Fund, the World Bank and the World Trade Organization – using intimidation, bribes, loans and military aggression – are now wiping out indigenous subsistence agriculture world around. The corporate giants are forcing poor farmers everywhere into positions where they must buy their seeds, fertilizers, even water from multinational corporations, must grow what the corporations dictate and must market through them at prices set by them.

Thus not only are the remaining sustainable agricultures being wiped out, but the people themselves are being subjugated. This is happening today. Even North American family farmers, through the corporate manipulation of patented seeds, are being subjugated. It is happening as you read this.

And independent greenhouse professionals, who at least often work with plants by hand, and who, one suspects, might just love their work, even these folks evince, umm, lack of creativity and initiative. They are, in most cases, spending tens of thousands of dollars in fossil fuels annually to heat poorly-designed greenhouses. In the worst case scenario they should cut their heating bills by 75% by following the advice in this book. In the best scenario their heating bills should be reduced to zero.

Though some of the answers here are new, most notably the "PSP" system and the "cold-sink" concept, others are as ancient as the earth and sun themselves. Since the 1970's there have been many dozens of books extolling the benefits of earth sheltering or passive solar energy collection. All folks have had to do is put the two concepts together, as we have been doing in North Idaho for the past quarter century, to slash heating and cooling bills and the attendant environmental degradation, and to grow and eat gloriously fresh, organic and nutrition packed vegetables and fruits year around. But few have even picked up on one concept much less the combining of the two. And so not only is America the poorer (paying for oil imports plus environmental degradation) but the professional growers – those who supposedly worship the bottom line – stupidly throw away tens of thousands of dollars for unnecessary fuel.

Though I seem to be singling out growers here, we Americans as a nation are equally to blame for arrogant over-consumption, what with our five percent of the world's population consuming twenty-five percent of  the resources and doing about the same amount of the polluting. There was a healthy movement in the 1960's and '70's to find sustainable alternatives, but that was wiped out in the Reagan '80s and has never really recovered. It is easier to let our corporations and armies pillage the earth rather than to roll up our sleeves and work out sensible solutions.

Bah humbug, America. A critic of U.S. culture and politics since the 1950s, I am still voraciously critical. Now, however, rather than being a beat or hippy outsider to the mainstream, I have, at 69 years of age, reached the respectability of ***Senior***Citizen***. My crumudgeoness must now be tolerated. Hobbling arthritically through my final years, I shall spew invective on all deserving. I shall flail my cane at all who venture near. Stand back, America. Stand back, you young whippersnappers.

CHAPTER 1
Prolog to a happy discovery

After buying my 40 acres in 1968 I made the unpleasant discovery that in our part of Northern Idaho we had only a 90-day, frost-free growing season. That shook my plans for a life on a self-sufficient homestead. How in the world was a guy's garden supposed to support him when nine months of the year most of his crops were frozen dead?

"Plant root crops," advised my old-timer neighbors, my mentors, "Potatoes, carrots. Put 'em in a root cellar and they'll last most all winter."

I did and it worked. I put the potatoes in sacks or in boxes or bins up off the ground and the carrots in pails of moist sand. Radishes, too, I discovered, would keep in moist sand. Apples, if they are "keeper apples", will over-winter beautifully. Others were having success keeping beets, parsnips turnips, onions, garlic, squash, and pumpkins, though not all of these are root cellar material.

I discovered the winter pleasure of home canned peas, string beans, corn, pickled beets, peppers and, of course, the wonders of cucumbers turned into dill pickles. Friends tuned me on to beef and venison jerky, and gave me home dried apple slices.

But where were the fresh winter greens? A pretty young Seventh Day Adventist cook in my favorite restaurant astounded me by making coleslaw from garden cabbage she had pulled up months before and hung upside down by its roots in her family's root cellar. Not prime stuff to be sure, but still edible and organically grown. I learned that if a guy was lucky and the snow melts, he can sometimes find in his dormant January garden a volunteer crop of green and edible wild winter cress. And you can count on wild dandelion greens in the spring before you can even think of working garden soil. There were other tricks like making tea from dried strawberry leaves. These brew into a beverage so strong in natural vitamin C that author Ewell Gibbons was thought to be salting with ascorbic acid the samples he brought in for testing – till the lab technicians went out and picked their own leaves to test.

But wouldn't it be nice to have home-grown, organic greens fresh from the garden nine or ten or even twelve months of the year instead of one to three months? I was getting tired of seeing my hard work go up in frost. Several years in a row I'd scurried along, same as my gardening neighbors, to cover the tomato plants at night in dread of the first killer cold, then finding that I was only extending the season a couple of weeks at best. Many hours of conscientious gardening work deserved more reward than that. I began a personal quest to find a passive, low-cost way of extending the growing season.

Here's the story of what I finally achieved near the Canadian border in a North Idaho mountain valley. For less than four hundred dollars I was able to permanently triple my growing season. I was also able to harvest some greens in the dormant winter season – a nine-month growing season with a twelve-month fresh harvest. Simultaneously I was able to drastically cut down loss from predators. This was all achieved without any energy other than my labor, the warmth of the sun and the warmth of the earth. How I pondered and stumbled into the earth-sheltered greenhouse and cold-sink concept is a tale in itself. So that you may have year 'round organic greens for pennies, and need not reinvent the wheel, I'll take you through my thought process, fumbles, discoveries and successes one by one. And I'll tell you how you (and I) can have even more gratifying successes in the future.

Chapter 2
The grow-hole concept

My quest to extend the growing season began when friends told me about the grow-hole concept. This is a technique that had been used by farmers in cold country for more than a century. A grow-hole consists of a pit two to three feet deep in which the bottom six to twelve inches has been backfilled with fresh horse manure, the middle is a layer of growing soil, and the top foot is growing space for plants. It is glazed by simply laying a window down on the ground spanning across the hole and packing loose dirt around the edges. No doubt many of the old-time farmers used storm windows for this. They'd be taking them off the house in the spring anyway.

A grow-hole allows you to plant garden plants a month or so early for subsequent transplanting into the garden when the danger of frost has passed. It can thus extend the growing season a month or more. Before electricity and central heat made indoor starts practical, it was a real boon to the gardener. A grow hole looks like this:

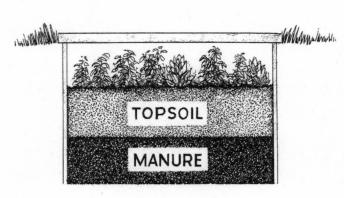

Here are the advantages of the traditional grow-hole.

1. It is down out of most of the wind.

2. There is little of what underground builders call "wind scrubbing". Wind scrubbing is what causes the "chill factor" in humans and animals on cold, windy days. It is what can make a day with a thirty-degree temperature seem like ten degrees. What that wind does to you it does to buildings and above-ground greenhouses also. Being out of most of the wind avoids most of the wind scrubbing.

3. A grow-hole utilizes the heat stored in the depths of the earth. It radiates up, warming both the soil around the roots and the trapped air in the space above. A grow hole traps, utilizes and stores the heat generated by the decomposition of the fresh horse manure.

4. Similarly, a grow hole traps, utilizes and stores much of the heat from the sun's rays.

5. By storing heat in the surrounding earth, a grow-hole moderates somewhat the effect of excessive heat trapped on sunny days.

Let's compare for a minute grow holes with the hoop and plastic system, a common method today of protecting seedlings and sometimes mature plants. This is when gardeners and farmers straddle the plants with hoops stuck in the ground over which they stretch polyethylene. This system is all right as far as it goes, but, trouble is, it does not go very far. A grow-hole is far more efficient at keeping the seedlings warm and it is important to understand why, for it illustrates the principle upon which this book is based.

Compare the two systems in their relationship to the air and the earth. Though the hoop system is generally used to cover long rows of plants, for the sake of illustration let's create a situation in which a grower might want to put a single plant, say a tomato start, under protection. Let's say he inserts two hoops into the ground a little more than a foot high at right angles to each other so that they form four sides and a top when wrapped with clear polyethylene glazing. Let's say that the four sides and top each have an area of one square foot and the protected growing surface beneath is also one square foot. When the sun goes down, the five surfaces rearing above ground will be losing heat while the growing surface below will be radiating heat from the earth's depths plus the sun's heat which has been absorbed near the surface during the day. If we call each heat-losing square foot a minus one unit and each heat-adding a plus one unit, we see we have a -5/+1 unit situation.

In the case of the grow hole the ratio is reversed. The growing surface adding heat is joined by the four walls also adding heat. Since there is only one unit losing heat, it is a -1/+5 unit situation.

A person would not be far off, probably, were he to conclude that a grow-hole is up to eight times more effective than the hoop and plastic method. But wait. We have forgotten the effect of wind scrubbing on the hoop unit so we can probably

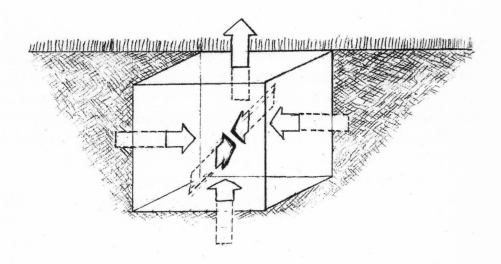

add another negative unit to that method, making it -6/+1. And we have forgotten that the horse manure is adding heat to the grow-hole so we can add another plus unit there. Then there is the fact that since the grow-hole is sunken it is down where the earth has lost a lot less heat than that on the surface through the course of a night or cold spell, and we're talking about five surfaces – add another two plus units. And, finally, since there is five times more surface area receiving and storing the sun's warmth at any given moment of sunshine, we should add a final two plusses, bringing the score to -1/+10 vs. -6/+1.

Now I'm not a mathematician or a scientist, and this is not a million-dollar research study, but it would seem to me a guy might speculate reasonably that the sunken grow-hole could be up to 14 times more effective in sheltering plants than the above-ground system.

This is not to knock the hoop system. There are a few advantages which we will mention soon that the hoop method has over the grow-hole. The hoops have their place. Elliott Coleman has had good effect using them inside his above ground greenhouses, and I saw this used in a greenhouse at a branch of Scotland's famed Findhorn community in the early 1980's. (In fact I was put to work in that greenhouse when the sun was shining and the air reeked of the polyethylene disintegrating from the ultraviolet rays. Within a half hour I had a headache and requested another assignment.) And there is utility on factory farms, where tractors do the cultivating and where there is a need to temporarily shelter long rows of crops. The long rows do cut down proportionately on some of the negative units on the hoop method, incidentally, when compared to our own one square foot example above. This is because in a 20' hoop row there is only one square foot of above-ground surface area on each end proportionate to the 60 sq. ft of surface area on the two sides and top, or a 2/60 ratio. In our one square foot example above the ratio was 2/3 or 40/60. If this has you confused, skip over it. We're merely trying to be fair and objective here, and to try to head off protests by advocates of the above-ground systems. We gave you that one square foot example only to stun you into realization of how miserably folks have failed to appreciate earth sheltering.

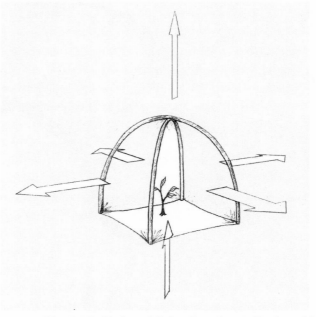

CHAPTER 3
The grow-hole in practice

I didn't have either electricity or a place with central heat those early years (all right, I didn't have a place at all – I was camping at first), and a grow-hole made a lot of sense as a way to start a garden early. So of course I made one.

It would be nice after that big build-up for grow-holes to be able to report my roaring success, but, alas, that is not the case: It was only moderately successful at best, maybe even less than that. I did not repeat the experiment a second year. This was back in the early '70s, now, and memory dims, but here is what I recall:

Almost immediately I had gopher problems. This was to be the first of decades of struggle with those #@%$&! demons.

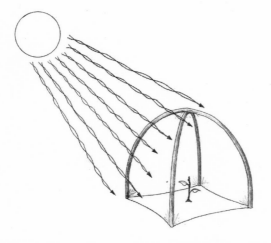

No, they weren't eating the plants as they would be soon in my garden. Instead, they began using the grow-hole as a dumping ground for the earth from their tunnels. I had built the economy version – had just dug a three-foot hole without siding it off with anything – figuring that the lower portion was going to be filled up with horse manure and growing soil anyway, and the top foot of earthen walls would be held in place by the roots of the grass surrounding the pit. It sounded good in theory. But the end result was the gophers discovered they no longer had to shove the earth uphill and out on the surface. They could instead just shove it horizontally out their tunnel with no care whatsoever about where it went, because it was not going to fall back in. The result was I was daily uncovering my seedlings and throwing the earth out of the grow-hole, doing much of the gopher's work for them.

The seedlings were taking a beating each time this happened, of course. Their leaves were coated with dust and mud — blocking at least half of the sun — and I was spending precious time blowing and shaking and washing off as much as I could, and neither the plants nor I were happy. Only the #@%$&! gophers were happy.

A second problem quickly manifested itself: the sides did begin to crumble and they began leaving gaps around the storm window used as glazing. I patched as best as I could with boards and earth, but cold air was seeping through nonetheless.

Those were problems due to lack of materials and time. Other problems, design problems, began presenting themselves. One was that the depth of the walls shaded the sun when it was low in the sky and in the morning and evening. Score one for the hoop and plastic method.

Sun low in the sky presented another problem: since the glass was horizontal to the ground, much of the sun's rays tended to glance off like a rock skipping over water. I later read that if the degree is great enough from perpendicular you can lose up to 95% of the rays. (This is not a problem with the hoop method – score another.)

Then there was the problem of what would happen if the roots of the plants reached the fresh horse manure below – say if you wanted to leave some of the seedlings in the pit to grow after transplanting the others. Or if you were late in transplanting. Wouldn't that burn the plants?

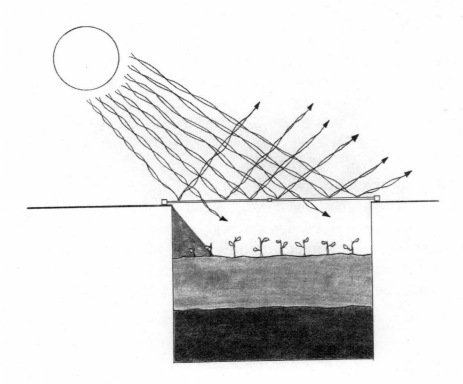

Finally, you had to open the grow-hole to work on the plants. This shocked the seedlings on cold days. No way to raise your young.

The grow-hole was not a success for me that year. I can't remember all the details, but I do recall that my transplanted seedlings were spindly, and that the plants I left in to mature did not produce and, in fact, did not survive. The former was doubtless the result of being buried often and also receiving too much shade from the walls. The latter had many causes, I think: the fact that I don't have a green thumb; that I was pretty new to gardening; that I was too busy working to make my land payments to weed and water properly; that the roots probably reached the manure. I think those were some of the factors. But think also the #%@&! gophers finally found the plants. That may have been the year that I saw one of my pea plants, waist high in a row of similar plants in my garden, begin to shake when none others were. Was it the wind? Then why weren't any of the other plants shaking? Earthquake? None of the others were quaking. I stood and pondered this phenomenon till I saw that the plant was beginning to sink into the ground. I stood there, mouth agape. I began to question my sanity. I was just a couple of years up from my California hippy days. Cold this be an acid flashback? Had I suddenly gone through the looking glass with Alice? What was going on? I watched with alarmed fascination as the rate of descent increased till the entire plant disappeared into the earth! I was stunned.

When I described this phenomenon later to my friends and mentors they smiled ruefully and shook their heads. "Gophers," they said.

I had met the enemy and he was #%$&! gophers.

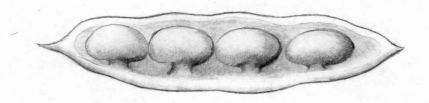

CHAPTER 4
The first cold-sink greenhouse

      I did not repeat my grow hole experiment the next year. Gophers and my poor results aside, there were a couple of things about the concept that looked like they could be improved upon. One was the pitch of the glazing. If you are losing significant growth rays because of the pitch, then why not correct it, or at least improve upon it? That should be as simple as piling the dirt from the excavation to the north and on a slant on the sides then resting the glazing on it. This would also give more growing space for plants which were taller and that you might wish to keep

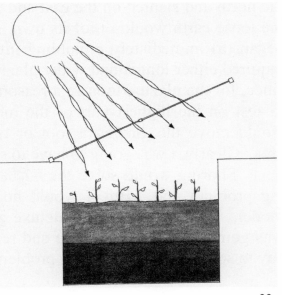

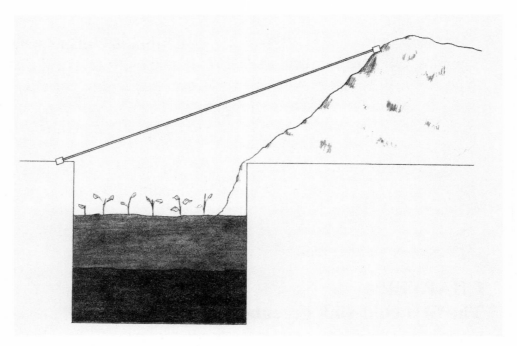

bedded longer, perhaps for the season. So that was my first improvement.

My second improvement came when it became obvious that I would need to shore up a grow-hole if I was going to improve the pitch this way. Vague memory recalls that the second year I actually got a new hole dug and the earth piled to the north and slanted on the east and west sides and that, since the loose earth wouldn't, of its own, stand in vertical walls, it began (a) immediately crumbling into the grow area and (b) required either longer and wider glazing or smaller grow space since, for the glazing to have a reasonable pitch, it would have to rest on the highest part of the mound to the north. That would move the glazing a foot or two away from the grow area. Clearly, I was going to have to shore everything up.

Shoring would solve the #@%$&! gopher earth dumping problem, too. But it would no longer be the economy model. It would be a super deluxe grow-hole. And if a guy was going to invest such time and resources, then wouldn't it pay to solve some of the other problems at the same time?

Like how about the problem of chilling the plants when opening the hole to work on them? If you were to avoid that, you'd have to work the plants from inside the structure. Which means it would no longer be a grow-hole now but would be considerably larger. It would be a "structure". It would be, in fact, a greenhouse.

More problems: We still have the shade factor caused by the low pitch of the sun blocked by depth of the south wall. Though this problem would lessen as the sun elevated in the sky towards summer, there would still be no sun there during the months when it would be most beneficial.

And there was the problem of just where a guy was to position himself to work on the plants. If you utilized the shaded area against the south wall – the logical place – you would find yourself cramped by the low glazing there. You'd have to work lying down or sitting bent forward. But if you worked against the north wall where there was head room, you'd be taking up prime growing space. That way you'd be

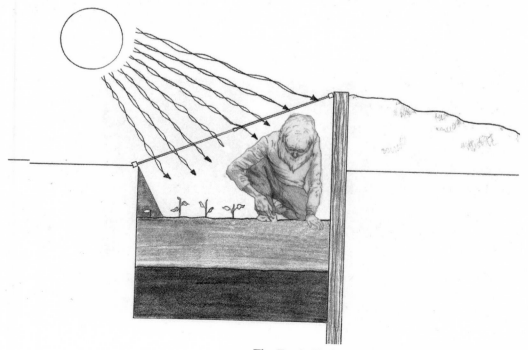

losing growing space against both of those walls.

What I finally decided was to dig a trench along the south wall in the shaded area to stand in while working on the plants. That way I would have headroom. And with a grow bed just three foot across, south to north, I could work all the plants by just reaching. I would never have to get up in the growing bed at all.

So that's what I built. I didn't realize at the time that I'd stumbled upon the "cold-sink" concept which was to make my

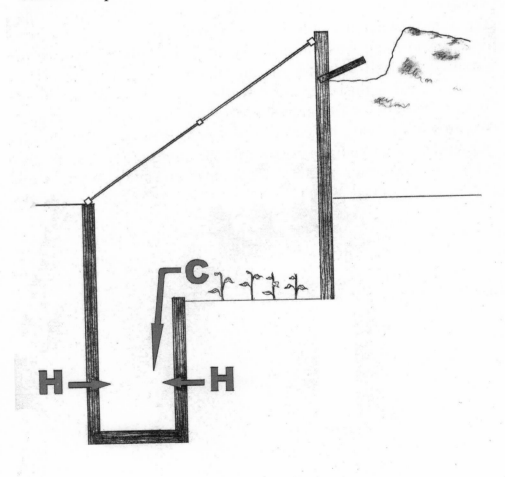

greenhouses four-season successes. The cold-sink concept is this, and it is this simple: The coldest air, which would sink to the otherwise lowest spot, the growing bed, now spills into the trench where it is warmed by the earth behind the walls.

The coldest air is removed from the plants passively, and it is warmed passively by the heat of the earth. This keeps it from stacking back up and covering the plants again.

This greenhouse had the additional benefit of the earth from the excavation which we piled behind the north wall. Not only did it eliminate any wind scrubbing against that wall, but now it became a heat sink in its own right. It was warmed by the sun all day and radiated the heat back into the greenhouse by night.

Let's go back to our heat unit method to calculate the efficiency of this earth-sheltered, solar greenhouse and compare it to that of a typical above-ground greenhouse of similar floor space. I can't remember the exact measurements of this first experiment, but these will be close enough: the grow bed was 3'x8' for 24 sq. ft. The floor of the cold-sink was 2'x8' or an additional 16 sq. ft for a total of 40 horizontal square feet. That's 40 square feet of horizontal surface adding heat or +40 energy units. The back, or north, wall was 5' high x8' wide, giving us an additional +40 heat units, minus 2 for a vent. That would be 38, then. The east and west walls of the growing bed were each 2'x3' or a +12 for the two. The south wall, the cold- sink wall, was 5'x8' for a +40 units. The north wall of the heat sink was 3'x8' for a +24, while its west wall was 2'x5' for a +10. The east wall of the cold-sink was a door and was a -10.

The rest of the minus units? Well, there was the south face, which was a glazed 8'x6' for a -48. The east and west above-ground walls each had 8 sq. ft of glazing for a -16. And there was a -2 for that vent we mentioned. All together, then, this first earth-sheltered greenhouse had a score of

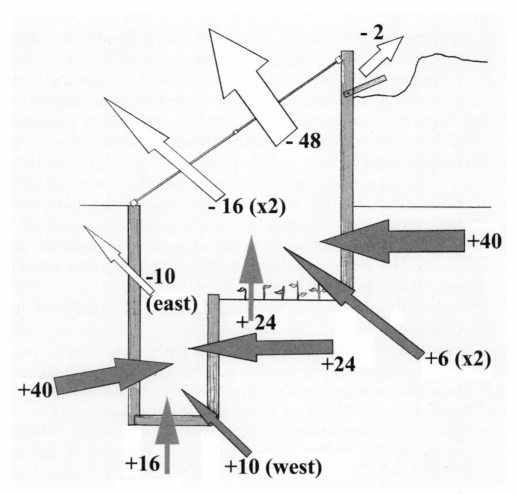

+164 and -76 heat units. That's 88 heat units to the plus.

How would a conventional 40 sq. ft greenhouse score? If we had one that was 5'x8' with 6' walls with a one-foot rise to pitch the roof, we would get 202' of exposed surface for a -202. Subtract a +40 for the heat arising from the earthen floor, and we come up with -162 heat units.

But again there are two more considerations that must be factored in. The first is that the earth in our earth-sheltered greenhouse, being below ground level, is going to be appreciably warmer throughout the night and during cold days than is that of the other which is on the surface. A reasonable guess is that it will add 25 per cent more heat per square foot than the other. So for reason of comparison factors we have to add +41 more units, making it now +207 minus -76.

And there is the wind scrubbing factor. This is a toughie to guesstimate. During the discussion before of the grow-hole vs. hoop and plastic method we gave a -1 unit for the five surfaces combined, or an additional minus 20% for each of the five -1 units. That is probably quite low. Seems to me a 20-mile-per-hour wind for any length of time on a 25-degree night could easily double the heat loss from an above-ground greenhouse over the loss of a still-air night. Ne'er-do-wells, oil company executives and other rascals may protest that a lengthy 20-mile-per-hour wind is rare and might only happen once in a winter – but once is enough. The plants need only freeze once for a greenhouse catastrophe. Now despite the fact that the additional -20% is probably quite small, we are going to use it

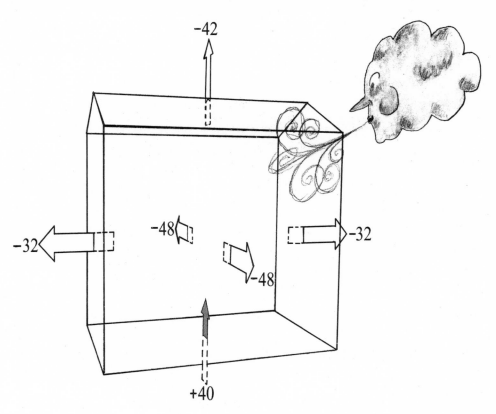

anyway, thereby squashing the hysteria of critics. We add another additional -40 units to the -202 for a total of -242 then for the above-ground greenhouse. Our earth-sheltered greenhouse gets an additional -15 wind scrubbing units for a total of -91 units. The final math then reads like this:

Above ground	Earth-sheltered
+40 units	+207 units
-242 units	-91 units
———————	———————
-202 units	+116 units

That means that this simple, earth-sheltered greenhouse is 318 heat units to the better compared to a similar above-ground greenhouse.

FINAL SCORE

COLD-SINK GREENHOUSE: +116 HEAT UNITS

TRADITIONAL ABOVE GROUND
GREENHOUSE: −202 HEAT UNITS

COLD-SINK GREENHOUSE
WINS BY 318 HEAT UNITS

Note: The earth-sheltered, cold-sink greenhouse calculated here has glazing on the east and west walls, totaling minus 16 units. We'll see in Chapter 16 that we are dubious about such glazing in northern climates. In many cases we think the better move is to berm earth out there, insulate it, cover the insulation with polyethylene and the poly with several inches of earth. That could turn those ends into heat sinks and give a + 16 instead of a -16 for a total plus of 32 more units to the earth-sheltered greenhouse, raising its score to + 148 and the comparison final score to a win of + 350.

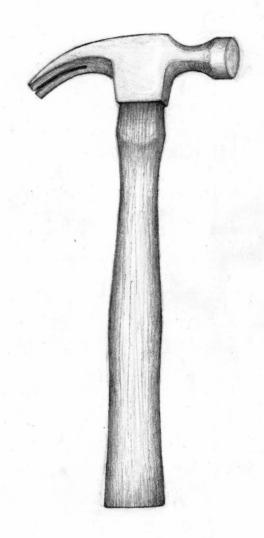

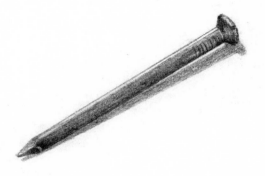

CHAPTER 5
P/S/P construction

Post/Shoring/Polyethylene, or P/S/P, is the method we developed when we built my original $50 underground house, as described in *The $50 & Up Underground House Book*.

The concept is simple: you construct a post and beam structure in an excavation and, before backfilling, you protect the lumber siding (shoring) from the damp of the earth with a layer of polyethylene.

Polyethylene is the stuff your plastic garbage bags are made of, only garbage bags are usually just 1.2 millimeter thick. In our construction we generally use material that is 6 to 10 mil. thick – excepting when we use multiple garbage bags themselves. Polyethylene comes in rolls of various sizes. We use it on both the walls and roof of our houses. For one of the two house roof layers, however, we are now beginning to use EPDM, the artificial rubber swimming pool and containment pond liner.

Post and beam itself is simple. You set posts that have been protected from the earth in some way into the ground, then notch girders into them for floor joists and rafters. Among several other advantages, this eliminates the need for poured concrete footings.

We have progressed through a number of methods for protecting the posts where they are in contact with the earth. In the original $50 Underground House we hadn't protected the posts at all and they, of course, rotted out and had to be replaced after ten or twelve years. In the $500 Underground House – which was an addition which tripled the original tiny (10'x12') $50 Underground House – we soaked the posts in a penta and diesel oil solution. When we came to our senses

and no longer were willing to use that poison method, we did some experimenting. One was to not sink the posts into the earth at all, but to set them up on concrete piers that we had previously poured in greased 6-inch or 8-inch stove pipe sections. When the concrete set, we removed the stove pipe for the next pouring. The concrete was reinforced with chicken wire and ¼ inch rebar which extended four inches out the top. We slipped the post down over the rebar via a ¼-inch hole drilled in the post bottom. This is the method we used on the hillside greenhouse.

The pier method has a built-in flaw which we anticipated from the start. We call it "hinging". This is when the pressure from the earth behind the wall pushes in hard enough to push both the post and pier into the structure a bit, as in the illustration. To avoid this, the post must be braced from the inside of the structure. This is a hassle and not always feasible, so we continued to search for other methods of post preservation.

One supposed old-time method we were told about involved soaking or otherwise impregnating stovepipe creosote into wood. We were told it was a common practice among farmers for their fence posts, and they only stopped when they were no longer heating with wood. This information was supposedly related in one of the Foxfire books, but to our disappointment we were never able to find it.

What we came up with in the end, and what we are using on our structures now, is what could be called the "Char/ garbage bag system" – not an intriguing title perhaps, but a descriptive one for a system that has worked well for us so far. It's a two-step process. The first step is to char the end of the post that is to go into the ground. We use small trees right off the land for the posts and peel them first. Where these are not available, a guy could use three 2x6's nailed or screwed together after the charring. We char them over a campfire till they have an eighth to a quarter-inch of charcoal over all the area that is to go two to two-and-a-half feet into the ground. This is another old-time farmer method of fence post preservation. Charring hardens the wood. It also creates its own creosote, for creosote, we are told, is the product of the incomplete combustion of wood. Not many critters, microbes included, want to eat creosote-laced charcoal.

Then we wrap the cooled, charred ends in plastic garbage bags, usually the full-sized black ones, though for greenhouse projects the smaller, white garbage pail liners might suffice. We have taken care before charring to make sure to cut off any sharp edges or protruding limb stubs that could tear the polyethylene. We use five bags as a rule, but put them on one at a time, pulling the surplus to the sides, then wrapping it around the post. We tape them in several places and take care to keep squeezing the air out of the bags so not to have any kind of a trapped bubble that could pop the poly when the earth is pressed against it during backfill. Then we dig holes with either posthole diggers or shovels and set the posts. The holes must be large enough to accommodate shovel handles all the way around because we usually tamp with shovel handles when backfilling. A number of other implements may be used for tamping of course – as long as they do not have sharp edges which may rip the polyethylene. We have previously staked out the site with batter boards, and run string to inform us of the outside boundary. That is, our posts will be set inside the strings and will just barely touch them. The holes, then, must stretch beyond the string to accommodate the shovel handles.

Setting these posts is pretty much a two-person operation. One holds the post while the other sees if it is plumb and begins the backfilling. Because of the irregular surface of unmilled trees, the easiest way we've found to check plumb is by the second person standing back and sighting down a plumb bob string visually aligned with the edge of the post. We do this from two directions, say the north and east. When the guy doing the reading is satisfied with the plumb, he begins the backfilling and tamping, but stopping to check every so often to see if the plumb is off. If a person is using milled lumber, say 6x6s, he might be able to tape two levels to the post and hold it with one hand while scraping in the earth with a shovel in the other, inverting it and tamping with the handle.

Correct tamping is an acquired skill and the most misunderstood part of post setting. The earth to be backfilled and tamped around the post must go in small increments, of perhaps 6 to 8 inch depth then compacted to perhaps half that before the next course is scraped or shoveled in. On a post sunk 2' to 3' in the ground, earth might be added six to twelve separate times during the post-setting process. If large amounts of earth are dumped at once, it will not tamp solid all the way down. Poorly-set fence posts wobble and fall, letting stock wander where not wanted. Poorly-set P/S/P posts will wobble out of plumb, making rafters difficult or impossible to align. In some cases poorly tamped and set posts can be dangerous. On big jobs where we have posts of 10' or more, we usually join the posts to batter boards with longer boards nailed on at an angle – diagonal bracing. And we brace extensively from post to post diagonally also.

The moisture content of the tamped soil is important. If it is too dry, it will not tamp well, if at all. It may be powdery, almost like talcum powder, and there is no way you are going to compress that with a shovel handle. For this reason, when we are digging and setting posts on a construction site in the heat of summer, we make sure we cover the excavated mounds with some plastic if we are not going to backfill immediately. Garbage bags ripped apart at the seam work well for this. If it's still too dry, we

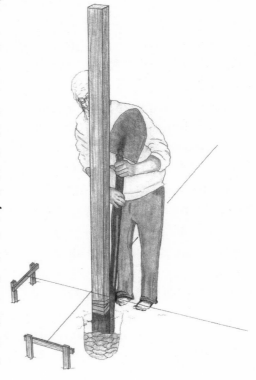

sprinkle on water and mix it up as though we were mixing concrete – though nowhere near that moist. Trial and error will
show you the right moisture content for solid tamping in your
particular soils.

The plastic covering will also protect from rain. Mud
does not tamp any better than powder, and after a good rain it
could take you days of sunshine to get it dry enough to tamp. A
worthwhile habit to get into is to cover the excavated earth immediately after the digging is done. Surprising how often you
get called away from any particular part of a job. It could be for
minutes, hours, weeks. In the majority of conditions, the earth a
couple of inches beneath the surface is generally of tampable
moisture content. Keep it that way.

You have to keep moving the tamper around. If you tamp
on only one side at a time, it may shove the post out of position
or out of plumb.

Setting the post two to three feet deep should keep the
post from pushing in from the pressure of the backfilled earth
behind the shoring. It will keep it from pushing in from down
below, that is. (Some engineers might question this. See Chapter 16.) The top part of the post is going to try mightily to push
in, and you must take a couple of precautions to prevent this. To
do so in the easiest, most effective manner, you must understand
two principles.

The first is that the best way to counteract the pressure
against one wall is with the pressure pressing against the opposite wall. This is not as hard as it sounds since you use the roofing girders and rafters (also called beams) for this. You have to
put them up anyway to hold the glazing, so make them do double duty.

The second principle is what I call "bone support". By
this I mean that the structural members transfer the pressure
from one unit to another with their bulk where they are joined –
not by the nails, bolts or screws that pin them together. To illus-

trate this, think of your leg. When you are standing, the thigh bone is directly over the shin bones. They are not joined off to the side somehow. Were they, you would probably be having knee trouble at the age of three, not sixty. The system works because the weight of your body gets transferred directly onto the top of the shin bones. The bones are stressed mostly compressively, not by shearing or bending.

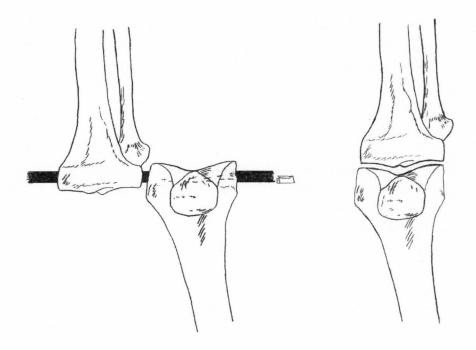

This is bone support.

The reason I stress this is because there can be more intense pressures on an underground structure than aboveground ones. This is especially true in areas with high ground moisture where the earth freezes solid for some feet below ground level. When the water in the earth freezes it expands, of course, and the pressures can become truly intense. For this reason alone it is advisable to not build underground where your soils consist of oozy clay.

I don't want to overdo this warning, but I have had sides of underground structures push in where I failed to follow the bone support principle. There are two places where it should be definitely followed.

When you are joining a post and a girder on the outer wall of a structure, be sure to notch so that the pressure bearing on the length of the post is transferred directly to the girder. That is to say, notch so that where the post and girder join, it is the portion of the post that is on the outside, not the girder. This puts the pressure against the girder and begins the transfer process across to the other side of the structure. If you put the post on the inside, it may likely over time be pushed into the structure, separating from the girder, making it look bad and weakening the place.

Assuming that your greenhouse is east/west oriented so that the great expanse of glazing is to the south, it is the north/south axis that is going to receive the most pressure simply because there is more wall, and most of it is in earth. This is particularly true of the north walls. If you have seven foot of rise in the back wall, and another five foot of north wall in the cold-sink, that's twelve foot of walls and pressure from one direction. And if it is on a hillside there is the additional factor of "hillside creep" – the whole hillside that is not solid rock is moving slowly downhill like a glacier. If you give it a chance, it will want to move into your greenhouse, seeing as how it is a hollow space in the earth and nature abhors a vacuum.

There is an additional problem on a hillside inasmuch as you are going to have moisture coming down from above and trying to back up against the back wall. It is not good at all if that water freezes so follow carefully our advice given elsewhere in this book on protecting that back wall from the water.

You are probably going to want to use milled lumber

(see Chapter 16 again) in making beams and rafters for the glazing. Here's how to attach them for bone support. Here also is how not to attach them.

Grievous Error

We made an engineering error on the hillside greenhouse shown on pages 165 and 166. It was a major cause of some posts pushing in. Because the greenhouse was built with mill ends of varying lengths, our post spacing was sometimes dictated by those lengths, making it impossible to always have the rafters lined up  with the joints in the glazing. So some of the posts did not have the direct bone support advantage of the rafters. We put the girder board, which spans between the posts of which some of the rafters are notched into, on the outside of the posts instead of inside. The rafters notched into that board kept it rigid and unmoving. When the pressure of the earth pressed against the posts via the other unsupported shoring, the posts pushed in, pulling away from the girder boards. Had the girders been on the inside of the posts, the rafters would have kept the girder board from pushing in and the girder board would have exerted pressure against the posts keeping them from pushing in also. The other boards in that wall — the shoring — are correctly located on the outside of the posts.

(Illustration A)

Illustrations (A), (B), and (C) show a good way of notching the post and rafter together but the girder board is on the wrong side of the post.

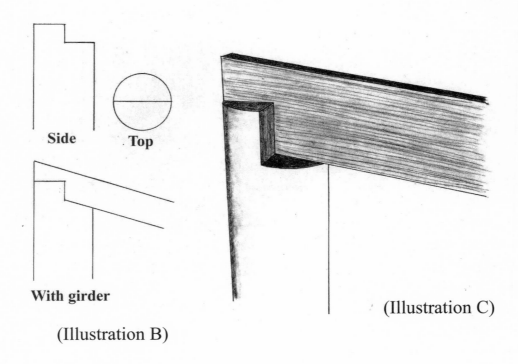

Side   Top

With girder

(Illustration B)

(Illustration C)

(Illustration D)

Illustration (D) shows what happens if a post isn't backed up by bone support: it pushes in from the top

Illustration (E) shows one effective way of dealing with the problem of the posts and rafters not lining up for bone support. Here by proxy the bone support is transferred to two rafters.

(Illustration E)

We refer those who wish to build with concrete blocks or other building methods to Rob Roy's excellent book *Earth-Sheltered Houses*, particularly Chapter Five, "External Walls", pages 97-115. See bibliography.

CAUTION CAUTION CAUTION

A reader of *The $50 & Up Underground House Book* phoned to alert the author to the possibility of earth walls collapsing on an excavation when building PSP. Right. Earthen walls collapsing and smothering workers are, in fact, the leading cause of work-related death among construction laborers. The first dead man this author ever saw (at age 5) was brought up after an excavation collapsed on him on 43rd Street on the South Side of Chicago. Twenty-eight years later, after three years as a union construction laborer, I recall peering down 12 feet into a ditch where four union laborers were working in the sand beneath Seattle and saying I wouldn't go down there for anything and shaking my head when they replied, "Aw, this shoring is strong. It'll hold." The morning papers reported the deaths of all four when the shoring didn't.

Earth has what is called an "angle of repose" which is the pitch it naturally comes to lie at. Sand and gravel have a low angle of repose — they move quickly to spread out. They cave in readily, in other words. The earth on the author's land, on the other hand, has a high angle of repose. It will sometimes stand at almost 90 degrees for a year or more with scant crumbing. It is for this reason I have had very little fear of being buried alive even though, of seven major underground projects on my land, six of them have been hand dug. There is also the factor that most of the digging has been done in fairly wide spaces, in houses, as it were, where if a wall of earth were to crumble it would be as likely to knock a guy aside as to bury him. The cold-sink is an exception. A guy could get buried in a cold-sink fairly easy. Especially if he is kneeling down working on, say, the lower boards in the wall. There is little area where the earth may spread out. Where it can go is on top. That is, on top of you, bub, should you be so unfortunate as to get yourself caught in that situation.

The two main ways of avoiding this are by shoring, which we have seen doesn't always work, and which, incidentally, is a real obstacle to try to work around; and by digging out the edges of the surrounding walls to where they are close to the angle of repose. What is the angle of repose for your particular soil? Ask your soil conservation officer. He can be found in the Natural Resource Conservation Service office in your county You can get a free atlas or DVD of your county soil profiles there too, including those on your own land. OSHA may also be able to help regarding the angle of repose.

As I have said, we have done most of the digging on my land by hand. The soil stands practically straight up. It rarely crumbles and has never threatened anyone in 35 years of digging. Nevertheless, when we are down in a cold-sink working on our knees, I have a couple of guys standing by with shovels to dig us out in an emergency. To some guys this seems like overkill (no, no, bad word … let's say overly cautious) but the fact is I have never had anyone so badly injured on my land as to require medical attention, and over the years I have let a couple of hundred greenhorns help with both construction and woods work.

Doesn't digging back your walls to the angle of repose, or near to it, doesn't that involve a lot of extra work? Ah, yes it does. And that's when it might pay you to hire an excavator or backhoe. Might pay you if your project is large anyway. Digging by hand, though it's great work (I enjoy it for two, maybe three hours a day) is very time consuming. And eager volunteers to help on such a project are scarce as hen's teeth these days.

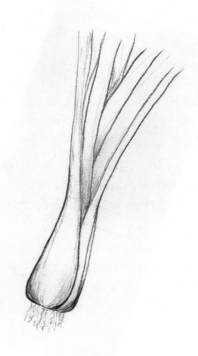

CHAPTER 6
Glazing

The glazing on your greenhouse is of paramount importance. It is where the growth rays and the heat of the sun enter. And it is where almost all the heat is lost during cold periods. Clearly it is the most important component in the structure.

The most commonly used greenhouse glazings today are the soft plastics. These include polyvinyl fluoride, polyvinyl chloride, polyester and, of course, the ubiquitous polyethylene. One estimate has it that up to 80 percent of all new commercial greenhouses constructed today in the US are glazed with a flexible film, usually polyethylene. This does not mean, however, that you should do the same.

Polyethylene has two big advantages over rigid glazings: It is the cheapest initially, and it is the easiest to work with.

These advantages seem irresistible to the commercial growers since they have yet to figure out that they need far less of the glazing than they currently use. They do not need glazing on the north side. What little ambient light they get from that direction can, I should think, be more than made up for with mirrors, reflective metal such as aluminum foil or white paint. (There is some surprising evidence that white paint may in fact be a more effective reflector than aluminum in greenhouses.) The north wall should of course be of wood, rock, concrete, brick, concrete block or other heat absorbing and releasing material, with waterproofing and a mass of earth on the outside.

Painting that north wall black, or other dark color, will increase the heat absorption from direct sunlight, but it will also eliminate most of the reflective sunlight to the north side of the plants. It is possible to mitigate this conflict somewhat with portable reflective panels that you might line the wall with during the growing months and remove during the months the plants are dormant, waiting for you to harvest them. They wouldn't need much of the growth rays then, but would need to draw extra heat to keep from freezing to death. As for a wooden wall — which is not the best heat sink — it might pay to paint it white from the start and have black-painted water barrels in front of it in the colder seasons. Worked right, this solid north wall would cut the growers' glazed surfaces 25% to 40% and a corresponding amount of heat loss. Most of the pros haven't figured this out in the last several centuries, though they probably will in the next twenty or so years when the cost of energy becomes truly painful. And when the cost of oil-based polyethylene continues to skyrocket. And when the polyethylene-covered greenhouses increasingly get devastated by the earth's increasingly heavy winds. And when the health hazards of working long hours in air polluted by the out-gassing of the polyethylene in sunlight are recognized.

The stuff you will be tempted to get, because it is so readily available at your local hardware store, the four-mil poly, is only going to last you a year because of those ultraviolet rays. If you send away to a greenhouse supply company for six-mil stuff that is specially treated for UV protection, which might last four years (assuming mild winds, a big assumption), you will find that the cost is no longer inconsiderable. It's a lot more than used windows which you can sometimes get for free if they are the old, single-pane wooden frame kind which nobody seems to want anymore what with everyone switching to the dual-pane, e-factored kind. Back-to-the-land legends, Helen and Scott Nearing, had those old used storm windows on the walls of their highly successful greenhouse more than seventy years ago — on the south wall, that is. The north was a heat absorbing (and releasing) rock wall, an early solar greenhouse.

Remember that you are going to have to replace that polyethylene every one to four years in the best of conditions (low wind and snow). There is both the cost of the material and the labor to factor. When you look at it that way it's not quite so cheap. Nor is it quite so easy to work with, either, considering that you have to repeat that labor again and again.

Glass

Glass is the historical greenhouse glazing. The ancient Romans had glass greenhouses. Until recently it has been the traditional glazing choice of professional greenhouse growers. It transmits light wonderfully. It doesn't decay and rarely deteriorates because of weather or chemical pollutants -- and never does so because of the ultraviolet rays from the sun. Nor does the sun's heat bother it. It will not buckle or warp on a really hot day like some of the plastics. It has very low thermal expansion, meaning that when it is well-installed and glazed it should not leak. It resists scratching and dirt better than the plastics. Also, it doesn't burn. It won't outgas the poisons so prevalent with the burning plastics.

The big disadvantage of glass, of course, is that it can shatter. This threat is mitigated somewhat by using double-strength B grade glass (DSB) which at 1/8 inch is twice as thick as regular window glass (single-strength B grade glass -- SSB). The DSB is considered usable in moderate sized greenhouses though there is a grade called greenhouse glass which is 3/16 or 7/32 inch thick and is presumably what the professionals use on the walls of their large greenhouses.

None of this type of glass should be used on the roof of a greenhouse or sunspace, however. If something hard and heavy should land on it, it will shatter into horrific shards which can do major damage such as blindness to those below who look up in alarm. Those who wish glass on their roof should use tempered glass. This stuff is four to five times stronger than window glass. It comes in 3/16, 7/32 and 1/4 inch. It resists wind, snow, thermal stress and impact, including hail. A glass dealer once told me that in a moment of extreme frustration he smashed his fist into a tempered sliding glass patio door, but all that happened was his hand was injured. The glass hadn't broken or even cracked. When it does break, however, tempered glass does not shatter into those dagger-like shards so common to window glass breakage. Instead, it crumbles into small pieces, almost into little balls, which are unlikely to injure.

Wire glass is another safety glass. It is ¼ inch thick with wire imbedded in it. You see this a lot in schoolhouse doors, and in glass that is around doors, or that otherwise comes to the ground — as it can in an earth-sheltered greenhouse. (A number of states mandate that safety glass be used when the glazing is within 16 inches of the ground.) Wire glass is also good for areas of high vandalism.

But besides shattering, glass has a second major disadvantage. Compared to most of the plastic glazings, it is hard to work with. It can not be nailed or screwed through, and in most applications it must be framed and puttied in. But most troubling is its weight. It can be up to five times that of the plastics, which can be a daunting prospect when hoisting it up by ladder for a roof application. Then there is the fact that you need a substantially stronger structure to hold it up there. Some of these disadvantages disappear, however, when glass is used on greenhouse walls. And much of the weight disadvantage is mitigated when glass is installed on earth-sheltered greenhouses because there you usually aren't climbing ladders when glazing the roof, but walking out at ground level on planks temporarily laid out on the roof rafters. This is so on most hillside earth-sheltered greenhouses. Yet even on flatland structures there is an advantage. It would be far easier and safer to wrestle a sliding glass door, say, up the mound of earth to the north than up a ladder. And, unlike most of the plastics, glass used in greenhouse walls gives the advantage of allowing views from the greenhouse — a big plus for those of us for whom gardening is a pleasure and therapy, and who live in beautiful, landscaped yards or rural areas.

A 1978 *Mother Earth News* article "Build Your Own Add On Greenhouse" said, "Regardless of what thickness or grade of glass you wind up using in your conservatory, each pane must be glazed properly. Fit it precisely into its opening with a little space all around and seat and seal all four edges with a first-class glazing compound."

Putty — which was standard for this job for years —- is difficult to work with and soon becomes brittle, falls away, and must be replaced. Forget it. The new, mastic-type glazing compounds are much better, and the plastic glazes even better yet. Both are extremely easy to install with a glazing gun. Never having had a large number of panes to glaze at once, my methods have been pretty elementary. I just bought whatever glazing compound was sold by my hardware store, would scoop out a bunch, roll it between my palms to make a long snake and press it all the way around the glass which I'd held in position already by several glazers points on each side. A putty knife would get it smooth and professional looking, though at times of desperation I have relied on my thumbs and even once a butter knife. I suppose in desperation a guy might be able to use an expired credit card. But use these only as last resorts if, say, you're a bachelor who can't find your putty knife which is in the kitchen utensil drawer because you've used it last to flip eggs when you couldn't find the spatula which was buried under magazines by the bedside after being used as an emergency fly swatter. A putty knife doesn't cost much and really does the job well.

Master apprentice jack-of-all-trades, David Fairall and I recently glazed a window using a putty gun, my first time ever. Truth forces me to admit I didn't know what a putty gun was, thought it maybe was a power tool like a staple gun or nail gun, or something. But when I went hunting for putty in that rural Idaho emporium, the Naples General Store, all I found was glazing putty in a tube instead of a can. This forced me to get an applicator which turned out to be nothing more than a caulking gun, which is a $2 metal device with a handle you squeeze to force the caulking or glazing out a nozzle. I'd been using one for years to apply caulking in cracks and gaps in my greenhouses where moss or cardboard or wadded paper wouldn't do the trick. (Moral: Don't feel dumb about what you don't know about construction. I've been in and out of construction for forty years, and I didn't even know what a lousy putty gun was. You are hereby forgiven your ignorance. Take the snickers with good humor.) Anyway, David and I fumbled our way along and got the job done.

Rigid plastics

As we have suggested, lightness and the fact that they don't shatter are reasons why many choose the rigid plastics for greenhouse glazing, particularly for the roofs. It is lighter than glass and requires considerably less support. It is easier to install. It won't break near as easily as glass and poses little risk of injury if it does. It has the advantage of diffusing the sunlight which allows it to reach parts of the plants straight sunlight can't. Most of the commercially-sold small greenhouse kits are constructed with the rigid plastics. However, if budget is your chief concern, you might well consider using used windows on the sides of your greenhouse and either second-hand tempered glass or one of the rigid plastics on the roof.

Unlike glass, which is great stuff when bought second-hand, neither the rigid plastics nor the films are good bets when acquired used. Since they deteriorate in time because of the ultraviolet rays of the sun, you may not know the true number of years they have been sun-exposed or what UV protection was factored in originally. But you can be sure you are getting less than if you bought new. The rigid plastics cloud up (yellow) and in the end block out most of the growth rays.

Some of the related materials are more resistant to this than others, and may be functional for as long as twenty years, but ten is the more common life span. I think most of the petroleum-based plastics deteriorate in sunshine over time. The common plastic glazings certainly do.

The rigid plastics have other problems. Most of them scratch easily and so lose some of their light transmission. They also expand and contract more than glass and need special fastenings to the greenhouse frame. With the exception of the acrylics, you can't see through them to the outside, which may detract from much of the pleasure of working in your greenhouse.

There have been four major groups of rigid plastics used for greenhouse glazing. These are fiberglass, FRP (fiberglass reinforced polyester), the acrylics and the polycarbonates. I've used the first two on greenhouses. On my original flatland greenhouse I used a roll of flat 'clear' fiberglass that I bought out of a 1970's Sears catalog. It wasn't clear at all but it did the trick anyway. It was easy to work with and cheap -- just the thing for a struggling, broke young homesteader. I've used the same stuff repeatedly since on my underground houses, filling in gaps between windows and in areas that are too small to warrant messing with glass. The stuff could be cut with tin snips in any shape desired and stapled to the 2'x4' framing. Staple it just to the outside and you had a four inch shelf on the inside. Staple it to both sides of the 2x4 and you had an insulated window. Not being a good carpenter or glazer made the fiberglass irresistible to me because of its ease of application. Had I not discovered it, the 'purity' of design on my underground houses would have been compromised. For it is my design principle that any part of my underground or earth-sheltered houses that are not earthen covered should be either glazed for light transmission or should be a doorway, preferably with a glass door. Had I known then what I know now about the combustibility of fiberglass, I might have had second thoughts about using it. But as it is it has served me well.

I used a second rigid plastic, this time a corrugated one, on the hillside earth-sheltered greenhouse. This was a FRP, brand name Filon. It was single wall and had little nipples of plastic embedded in it on the underside which, it was claimed, would magnify the sunlight. I don¹t know whether it did or not, but I did have some great crops in that greenhouse for the first ten years, the length of time the Filon was warranted to stay clear and transmit growable sunlight. After that the crops began to dwindle miserably until it was not worthwhile planting the greenhouse anymore. It is because of the vulnerability of both fiberglass and the FRPs to degradation by the UV light -- plus their scary combustibility -- that they are rarely used in commercial greenhouses anymore. That, and the fact that the films seem so cheap on the initial application.

With the Y2K computer scare in the late 1990's I re-glazed the hillside greenhouse in a rigid, corrugated, single-sheet plastic which may not have been designed for greenhouses. I can¹t even remember what I bought. It was whatever was on hand at my local building supply. It worked, but not as well as the Filon. Moral: do your homework before glazing.

Among the several things to consider are whether you are going to use single sheet or a thermopane, double-wall type of glazing. The single sheet has several advantages. It is lighter, easier to work with, and does not require quite so much support structure beneath. It is also considerably cheaper and admits more of the growth rays. However, moisture condenses on it and may drip down on the plants, causing disease and mold problems particular to greenhouse growing. There are chemicals that may be sprayed on the underside of it which encourage the droplets to run down to the earth on the sides of the greenhouse rather than drop on the plants. But then again you are adding another dubious chemical to your environment — your food-producing environment at that.

Water will normally not condense on the double-wall glazing. And the glazing is stronger. But the great advantage of double-wall glazing of course is that considerably less heat will escape through it in cold weather — a higher R rating. Combined with an earth-sheltered greenhouse that has a cold-sink, this is pretty much an unbeatable combination in cold climates. And depending upon your climate, there will be fewer times, if ever, that you will need to fuss with insulating panels.

Back to the rigid plastic glazings...

Acrylic (Plexiglas, Exolite, Lucite, Polycast) is a fascinating material which transmits light and is nearly as clear to see through as glass but is much stronger, up to seventeen times stronger by one calculation. It is so strong, in fact, it is what is used for airliner windows, and windows in vehicles which cart around presidents, popes and the like. It's what is between you and a teller in her armored booth since a little over an inch of thickness makes it "bullet resistant." Most sources claim acrylic will transmit growth rays well up to 25 to 30 years, depending upon care and additives. One source, however, wisegeek.com, insists, "There are some misconceptions about acrylic. namely that it yellows, turns brittle and cracks over time... If taken care of, acrylic remains new-looking, regardless of age or exposure to sun. Some people worry that acrylic scratches too easily, but unlike glass, scratches can be easily buffed out..."

They are unlikely to be as easily buffed out on the roof of a greenhouse, however, which may be one reason Plexiglas, et al, aren't used in greenhouses that much. These acrylics, like most of the plastics, also have a much higher thermal expansion than glass, necessitating special procedures to fasten it to a greenhouse frame. And they may sag if the temperature gets over 180 degrees, which can occasionally happen near the roof of a greenhouse. In fact, with enough heat they will melt or even burn, though their combustibility is nowhere near as bad as Fiberglas or FRP. But probably the biggest problem with acrylic is cost. In most cases it costs more than glass — and many times more than used glass.

The winner these days — the rigid plastic most often chosen for greenhouse glazing — is polycarbonate. Single polycarbonate panels (i.e. Dynaglass, Macrolux Corrugated and Lexan Corrugated) are said to have a light transmittance of 94%, about as good as there is in the business, including glass. Double wall polycarbonate panels (i.e. Polygal, Macrolux and Lexan Dripgard) have light transference of 83%, also excellent. This material is lightweight, rigid and relatively strong. It may be screwed through and sawed. They are somewhat resistant to UV damage and untreated may be expected to last ten years. Treated, the panels may be good for twenty or even twenty-five. Read the warranty before buying. Though they scratch easily they are less combustible than acrylic and, especially, FRP. They do have considerable thermal expansion and thus require special fasteners to the green-house frame. But for their weight, ease of use, light transmission, UV resistance and cost, they seem to many the best buy among the rigid plastics.

Double-wall polycarbonate panels are what I plan to use on the next greenhouse roof. I doubt I'll use it on the south wall since it is costly compared to used windows. Plus you can't see through it, and it deteriorates in the sun in time. Used glass windows will be my choice there, maybe common glass windows for the vertical sides, but certainly used sliding glass doors set in permanently for walls that tilt at an angle. But for the roof? Yeah, I suspect I'll probably go with double-wall polycarbonate.

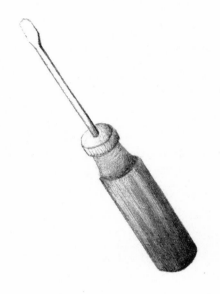

CHAPTER 7
Insulation

If your greenhouse is in really cold country you might well consider insulating your glazing for night and for cold, cloudy days. With today's wonder materials this can be easy and relatively inexpensive. The principle is simple: secure insulation beneath the glazing. You will likely do this between the rafters. You will want a lightweight, rigid material that can be put in place in a quick, easy manner and which can be as easily removed and stored. In most cases this would suggest the rigid plastic foams.

The three classic foams are polystyrene, polyurethane and polyisocyanurate. All three have great R-values which is the measurement of a substance's resistance to heat transmission, its insulating value – as opposed to its ability to transmit heat well, its K-value. The R-value of polystyrene (Styrofoam is one brand name) is 5.0 per inch, polyurethane 7.0 per inch (decreasing in time to 6.3 after out-gassing) and polyisocyanurate 8.0 when backed by aluminum foil such as on the brands Thermax and High-R Sheathing. It should be noted that while aluminum conducts most heat well – a high K-value indicating a poor insulator and the reason many replace the older aluminum frame windows with vinyl frame windows – aluminum also reflects a certain kind of heat. It reflects far-infrared radiation, or far-IR. This is the kind of heat that bodies, the earth, and thermal masses radiate. When this radiation strikes a surface, it warms it and in turn transfers the heat in the form of another wave length to the ambient air mass. When it strikes plants and other objects within a greenhouse, it is all to the good since it warms the interior air mass. When it strikes exterior glazing, however, that is not nearly so good. It warms the glazing and much of it is then transferred and lost to the outside air. This reflective quality of aluminum of the far-IR is the principle which makes "space" or "survival blankets" so effective under conditions of extreme cold – it reflects body heat back to be reabsorbed. Since there is so much glazing in a greenhouse, it may repay you handsomely to include a layer of something aluminum when you build your insulating panels. Aluminized Mylar is a brand often used in this context. It is a thin sheet of aluminum sandwiched between Mylar sheets, making it many times more durable than plain aluminum foil.

All the foams usually come in 4'x8' sheets of one to three-inch thickness. Two-inch thickness or more might be recommended for your project since it will have greater strength and should hold up better under frequent handling than one-inch. All three foams may be cut with a knife or saw, though if the latter is used with polystyrene (Styrofoam, Fermafoam, Fome-Cor and Beadboard) the dust will cling to every surface. Polystyrene foam must not be painted with anything other than latex paints, incidentally, as the others will dissolve it.

All three foams have flaws which can be deadly:

(1) They are flammable.
(2) They emit toxic or lethal gas when they burn.

I shudder still when I recollect stories from the 1950's and '60s about large domes and Quonset huts housing chickens which caught fire in the foam-lined interior. The fire flashed around the dome in a sheet of flame in seconds and in less than a minute the cyanide gas killed all the birds, thousands of them.

That's frightening. It is the reason why such foam used in house and office construction is accompanied by non-combustible materials such as plaster board pressed against it. It makes a person think seriously about using it in construction at all. The good news is that this hazard is not nearly as great in greenhouses tended by alert workers as in homes where people asleep may not detect a fire's early start. Homes may have additional fire hazards such as flammable liquids, cooking fire, defective wiring, smokers and kids playing with matches. Few of these conditions apply to greenhouses.

What does apply to greenhouses, but perhaps not to homes where the rigid foam insulation is rarely exposed, is that sunlight breaks down many plastics, releasing toxins.

This of course should be of concern in greenhouse insulation. My own particular rule of thumb here is that if you can smell the plastics when they are in the sun, they are outgassing. I do not know at this point in time just what gasses they exude, but they are certainly not to be trusted. All exposed foam surfaces should be either aluminum foil-covered or latex- painted.

Or you can make your own insulating panels out of cardboard. It is best if you can get the large discarded cardboard from appliances and furniture stores, but even grocery store throw-aways will work if you overlap the material in layers as bricks overlap each other on a wall. You glue it all together and press it for some hours to give it shape. You do not want to crush it, however, as it is the air pockets in the cardboard which is the prime insulating factor. Add aluminum film or aluminized mylar and duct tape the edges. You should paint the whole thing except perhaps the aluminum section to protect it from moisture. These cardboard panels are going to warp on you eventually and any lightweight reinforcing you can muster up and incorporate in the layers might pay for itself down the line. Though not as good insulation as the foams, the cardboard should not outgas near as much nor should the smoke from its combustion be near as toxic. And you can't beat the price. There's even a company, Simplex Industries, that manufactures a line of inexpensive house shutters from dense cardboard sheets with aluminum foil on one side and white paint on the other.

Or you can try another material, Foamglass, manufactured by Pittsburgh Corning. Though both thicker and heavier than most of the other foams, it still is light enough to make good window shutters. Best of all, it is nonflammable. This rigid material may be cut to shape and painted. It's R-value is reportedly 2.5 to 3 per inch.

Here's all you need to do to make rigid foam insulating panels.

1. Select and purchase the insulating material. If the material does not come backed with aluminum, buy sufficient Aluminized Mylar or the equivalent and tape it to the side of the insulation which will face into the greenhouse. You will also need a roll or two of duct tape, some paint, some wood scraps and at least four wood screws per panel which are long enough to hold the wood scraps in place as fasteners.

2. Cut the panels a little smaller than the space they are to insulate, maybe an eighth of an inch smaller to allow for the bulk of the tape. Then tape the edges to help reduce wear. Number the panel and the place where it will be hung.

3. Make a couple of handles or tabs to facilitate the handling of the panels in and out. Do not use wood and screws as they will tear out of the foam. Use instead the duct tape itself. Do this by applying tape first on the "up" side of the foam, the side that is to face the sun. Bring the tape down across the edge of the foam and out on the down side, maybe two inches. Then, without cutting the tape, unroll another two inches and bend it in against itself, sticky surface to sticky surface. That's your tab. Continue unrolling the tape for an other sev-

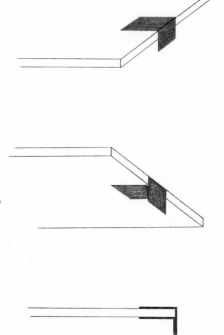

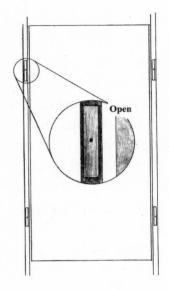

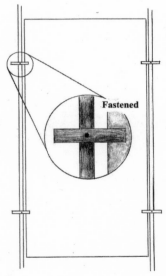

eral inches and press it against the underside of the panel.

4.   Paint the up side of the panels to protect them from disintegrating in the sun's rays. Number them and the spaces they are to fill.

5.   Make fasteners by screwing bits of lumber scrap to the rafter. When the length of the scrap is parallel to the rafter, the panels may be inserted or removed. When it is perpendicular it holds the panel in place. You probably made some of these latches as a kid. They still work.

6.   The panels may be stored in the cold- sink when not in use.

INSULATING THE EARTH

Depending upon your budget, you may want to insulate the earth itself around the greenhouse to turn it into a heat sink. This concept applies mostly to the north wall which receives the most sunshine. And it is especially beneficial on flatland earth-sheltered greenhouses which have a north wall which usually rears up several feet above the surface and is backed with a mound of earth. Rearing into the atmosphere, that mound of earth will chill far more quickly and far colder than the rest of the earth around the greenhouse.

The concept is simple: take off some earth to use later,

then rake the earth of that north mound into flat planes. Cut rigid foam insulation to fit and lay it out on the planes. Cover the whole thing with a polyethylene sheet and cover that with six or more inches of earth to protect it from the sun. You may plant in it grass seed if you wish, but the grass will probably die unless watered frequently since the roots can not draw on the ground water due to the poly and insulation barrier. Crownvetch from rootstock has worked well for me in similar situations. It spreads of its own accord, is drought-resistant and chokes out weeds. It thrives in most climates in both sun and partial shade. Or, if you can be patient and are willing to replace the eroded earth periodically, nature will plant it for you. Some straw on top will minimize the erosion and enrich the soil.

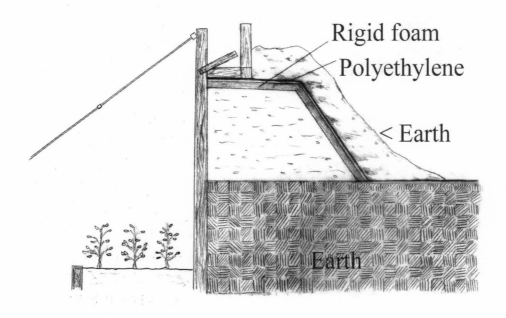

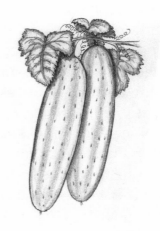

CHAPTER 8
Ventilation

One of the several great things about shed roof construction is its ability to channel heat through a structure. If it is properly designed, you could heat an entire 2,000 square foot underground house with a single wood stove operating in the lowest sector. Because of convection currents, the heat rises up automatically through the rooms and hallways. A little experimentation with how open you leave the doors or other air channels (bring back transoms?) gives you the right combination for central heat in such a structure with no technologically complicated, failure-prone delivery system.

This effect is equally valid when venting a shed roof greenhouse on a hot day. That shed roof acts as a chimney. I first noticed this effect on my original $50 Underground House in 1971 when I would light a campfire outside the "fire window" which was on the lowest side of the house next to my bed. It was mighty comfortable, believe me, to lie in bed at night just a few feet from a small outside campfire. Except for one factor: the smoke inevitably drew up through the house because of the shed roof. Smoke does not enter my house, on the other hand, when I cook over an open fire through the "barbeque windows" which are on the other side of the house, the uphill side, facing into the Uphill Patio (see *The $50 & Up Underground House Book*.) That is on the high side of the shed roof. It is in effect at the high point of the "chimney". To enter the house there in any amount, the smoke would have to draw downward, which, as we all know, smoke generally does not want to do.

Now, the same effect works for the shed roof greenhouse. You create a chimney effect by opening vents at the very top of the glazed shed roof, and at low points also. The hottest air rises out the top vents, pulling cooler air in from the openings below. This is so successful that on one of my greenhouses when I stood with my face to the outside of the upper vent, my face was cooled with an air current of a couple of miles per hour, a virtual breeze. Because of sound design the place was venting itself automatically. There was no power involved other than that provided by the sun and gravity. There were no electricity bills involved, no wiring or motor installation costs. There was no power to be disrupted, no fans to fail. The system is as dependable as the sun and gravity.

On the large commercial greenhouses I hope to build someday, I will have the top four foot of the shed roof in plywood that I can open on hinges for summer ventilation and sunshine and some of which I may keep closed for shade on the hottest of days. Yet on two of the three greenhouses I've built, I've done well with just vents built into the highest part of the back wall, the north wall. It is vital that you position these vents at the highest possible part of the wall or roof.

I have seen above-ground, peaked-roof greenhouses built by unfortunate souls who didn't realize the necessity of venting at the very top. They thought that just opening ground level doors at either end would do the trick. But it rarely did, and their plants often wilted and died on hot days. Even putting a fan in one of the doors did not work well

unless all of the surrounding door opening was blocked up – it was easier for the air to just pull in from the doorway around the fan rather than from the doorway clear across the greenhouse. Smarter folk put fans in the end wall above the door and kept it closed while opening the opposite door. In my

fuzzy memory of youth I seem to recall some professional greenhouse owners using such fans. I'm happy to report that today many folk are using a totally passive venting method up at the very apex of the peaked roofs. This has been made possible by the development of "automatic arm" openers which operate by the heat expansion of oil which drives a piston. I dimly recall the prototype of this as having been invented by a 1960's hippy homesteader sort of person who used mercury as the original expansion fluid. Or maybe I just read about them first in the early *Whole Earth Catalogs*. But in any event they can be a blessing for those who cannot give full daily attention to their green-houses. This, of course, would include many earth-sheltered greenhouse owners.

automatic vent arm

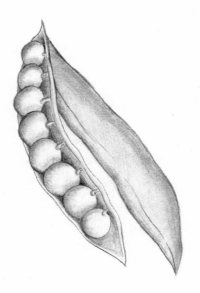

CHAPTER 9
Passive solar
energy collection

Some years ago there was a big trend towards "solar greenhouses", meaning greenhouses which in some way collected and stored the sun's warmth for nights and cold days. It was a worthy endeavor and resulted in a spate of books on the subject. A year ago when I was researching this on the Internet I think I counted more than thirty such books. Too bad the authors didn't catch on to earth-sheltering also, for they go hand in hand. They are in fact the same, for the earth's crust and bodies of water are the greatest solar collectors of all. Unless the crust is venting the heat from the earth's interior – as it does in areas of hot springs and such –

the warmth of the surface of the earth and some feet below is the result of the sun's rays. That's why at eight feet down the world around the temperature stays at the climate's yearly mean temperature. Utilizing those phenomena is the primary reason for this book – witness the cold-sink. In the chapter on insulation we have suggested ways of further enhancing earth/solar storage by strategic use of insulation in the earth some feet out from the north walls. Now we are going to suggest two other ways of passive solar collection within greenhouses. But first an explanation of passive and non passive solar heating.

A non-passive system might involve a house or greenhouse which has a mass of crushed rock beneath its floors through which is blown air heated by the sun. The heated crushed rock then either radiates the heat back passively into the structure during the cold hours, or transfers the heat via (again) mechanically-blown air. Another form of non-passive heat collection and storage could utilize solar hot water collectors on a roof from which hot water is pumped into holding tanks in the house below.

"Passive solar collection" means capturing the sun's warmth directly into the storage mass, the "heat sink" and letting it radiate out later into cooler temperatures without any use of mechanical devices whatsoever. The sun directly heats a mass, and the mass directly releases the heat to cooler air later.

In my earth-sheltered greenhouses we stretch out the structure on an east/west axis to get this benefit of a long, sun-drenched north wall above the main growing bed. This offers an excellent opportunity for passive solar collection. If made from stone, concrete or concrete block, the north wall itself may be a passive solar collector, and a good one. Making such a wall thicker than normal should give you increased thermal storage, and strategically-placed insulation will also increase the thermal usefulness. On flat land, insulating the entire mound of earth behind the wall as described earlier should prove worthwhile, whereas on a hillside just insulating behind the masonry itself, at least the top three feet, might prove beneficial enough. Take care to keep that wall from pushing in from the lateral thrust of the earth by sinking the wall a couple of feet below surface, tying in the top of the wall to the top of the south wall with the 2x6's holding up the glazing (our bone support concept) and by reinforcing the center of the wall with either rebar or a reinforcing plaster such as surface bonding cement.

A less expensive and quicker way of getting a passive solar collector in the greenhouse is to place dark-colored steel, 55-gallon drums of water against the PSP back wall. You don't want to fill them all the way up, and you want one of the bung caps to be loose to allow air flow during temperature changes. This will allow the water to expand and contract without crushing the barrel. Also frequently recommended is a slight layer of oil on the surface of the water. That way when the water level lowers with temperature contraction any exposed interior metal is lightly coated with oil and will not rust. To keep the bottoms from rusting out in contact with the soil, elevate them up an inch or so on bricks or boards. Dark painted, plastic 55-gallon barrels are also used for this, though I don't think they transfer the heat as well and, being plastic, must deteriorate in the sun light. On the other hand, they won't rust.

The tops of the barrels may be used to support potted plants either on planks or on the tops of the barrels themselves. (In a luxury model greenhouse you will want to build a permanent table or bench above the barrels to facilitate servicing the barrels or removing them during the warm months for other use of the space.) Above the barrels is a great place for our sprawling, tall-reaching tomato plants. If they are planted on ground level in front of the barrels, they will shade the barrels, lessening the ability of the water within to absorb and radiate heat. Also the tomato plants should survive a couple of weeks longer in the cold weather, seeing as they are up higher where the warm air has risen, and because the barrels are radiating heat directly up to them. This passive use of the warm air rising requires no failure-prone outside energy source.

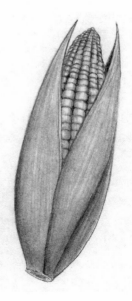

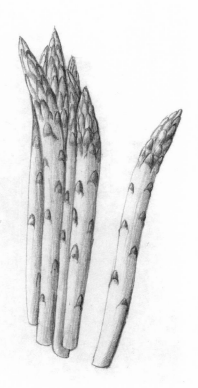

CHAPTER 10
Heat tubes

Friend David Ronniger, of Ronniger's Seed Potatoes, suggests that I tell you about two greenhouses that he saw in the mountains in Colorado, both at 8,000 foot elevation. Even on the coldest nights when the temperature dropped well below zero, the greenhouses maintained a base temperature close to 52 degrees for almost no energy outlay. The owners of the greenhouses had to merely raise the temperature another twenty or so degrees for optimum growing conditions. Fifty-two degrees is a 62-degree head start on a -10 degree night. They achieved this effect by employing heat tubes, two-hundred-foot-long tubes buried six to eight feet deep in the earth. At the distant end the tube rises above ground and snow level and is an air intake. Below surface, where the intake bends toward the greenhouse, there is an electrically-driven fan which pumps the air through the pipe. During the course of its travels the air is warmed to 52 degrees by the earth. It is released into the greenhouse through pipes all along the base of the south wall where it can circulate freely through the rest of the structure. All it costs for this free heat is the small amount of energy needed to run the fan. Running the pipes up-hill to the greenhouse should help even on that small energy bill by encouraging the heated air to rise of its own accord.

This is not a system for the small hobby greenhouse owner. A ten- or twelve-inch plastic pipe is costly, as is the digging and backfill of an eight-foot deep, two-hundred foot-long ditch. And it certainly would play havoc with an established lawn. Your earth-sheltered greenhouse cold-sink will achieve most of the advantages above with very little initial cost and no running cost. But for professional growers in certain climates the heat tube concept is almost a must. And it has one advantage over a cold-sink: it brings in outside carbon dioxide. This advantage is nullified in a greenhouse that has rabbits in the cold-sink and/or fowl up next to the water barrels.

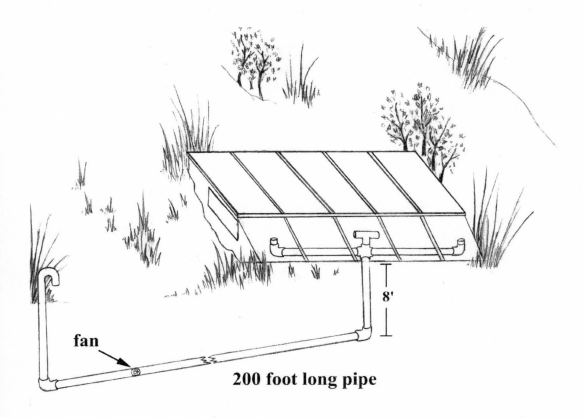

fan

200 foot long pipe

8'

CHAPTER 11
Bugs and other pests in your greenhouse

I've never had a rabbit, deer, elk, moose or bear plunder my greenhouses. They've raided just about everything else on my land, but not my greenhouses. Though bears could rip their way in – two have broken into my underground house, the most recent in 2004 – and though they love fresh greens in the spring, I think the rewards just don't smell great enough. Why bust into a place when there are farm fields in two directions with tender young alfalfa and wheat and rye sprouts in abundance?

The structure seems formidable enough also to fend off all hoofed animals, save perhaps a moose. But those guys love food found in marshes and rarely cross my land. However, many millions of people around the world can attest to the damage a couple of deer can do to a garden in a single night, much less repeated nights. A greenhouse is a pretty sure deterrent. And if you are in a theft-prone urban or rural area, you can lock your garden up from two-footed marauders at night, too.

Plenty of other critters have raised havoc in my greenhouse, though. I've been hit with white flies, grasshoppers and gophers; mice, carpenter ants and (again) gophers in the two greenhouses I've cultivated long enough to attract the pests.

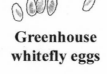

Greenhouse whitefly eggs

Greenhouse whitefly pupa

These are the pests I've recognized, anyway. There were doubtless others.

The white flies multiplied rapidly in the second or third season I had the garden house greenhouse planted. They loved the tomato plants and were doing a job on the leaves. Answering a magazine ad, I bought two bright yellow plastic disks which I smeared with baby oil and hung near the plants. Presto, I was catching them by the thousands. Attracted by the yellow, they got stuck on the oil. Looked like dandruff on a computer keyboard. When the disks were nearly covered after several days, all I had to do was wipe them off with a paper towel, oil them, and hang them again. After a couple of weeks the white flies were under control.

Then grasshoppers appeared one August day and began multiplying rapidly. They began devastating my lettuce and

> **Most illustrations of bugs in this chapter are greatly magnified.**

Greenhouse whitefly

Swiss chard. I had no idea of how to get rid of them organically till I thought…flyswatter! Worked great. Twenty minutes the first day then decreasing times every several days thereafter and the problem was licked. Made great trout bait. Never did fry them up, though some swear that grasshoppers are "the shrimp of the plains."

Then, alas, there were the gophers. Those louts of the loam about ruined the garden house greenhouse. I remember flooding their runs with the garden hose and worrying about flooding out the attached house. It never did flood out, but I never got rid of the gophers, either. That was one of the factors causing me to disuse that particular greenhouse. That and the fact that the focus of activity moved over the ridge to the south, the ridge causing all the shade. On the south slope the micro-climate gave us a month earlier spring every year and twelve months of sunshine, or what passes for winter sunshine here in the Pacific Northwest.

We built the hillside greenhouse on that south slope around 1979. That's the green-house in the colored pic-tures on pages 166 and 169,

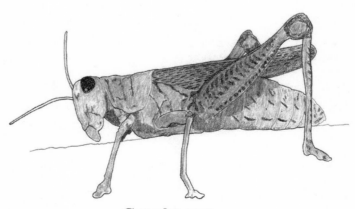
Grasshopper

the structure that gave me some still live tomato plants on the 17th of December, 2004, and live kale, Swiss chard and lettuce clear through the winter. I discovered this on the 6th day of February, 2005, when I approached the greenhouse, assuming that all had perished inside. I hadn't attended the greenhouse in more than six weeks. The plants hadn't been watered in all that time, and we had had a cold snap where the temperatures went down into the single digits.

So how could the plants survive all that time without water? Obviously there was some in the soil, and obviously the sun was not parching it in January at those temperatures and with the scarce Northwest winter sunshine. Then, too, there was some mulch on top of the soil. But we know most plants don't grow at temperatures below 40 degrees. Do you suppose the hardies maybe go into a sort of hibernation at below freezing temperatures? They wouldn't need much water then. Anyway, on the 6th I gave the survivors a drink and on the 12th I harvested.

But we were discussing pests. The hillside greenhouse has had three main troublesome ones: ants, mice and #@%-$&! gophers. The ants and mice seem to eat the tender seedlings. The #@%$&! gophers eat everything else. The ants infesting my greenhouse are carpenter ants, big folks with two-tone bodies, red and black. They don't eat wood like termites do, but they do tunnel into wood, making honeycomb-like tunnels for their nests. I can't swear they eat my seedlings, but observation tells me that the seedlings disappear closest to their nests first. When I go to war with their colonies, the seedlings survive.

There are 15,000 to 20,000 carpenter ants in a single colony, not to mention its satellites and suburbs. Which describes my hillside greenhouse. Being almost entirely of wood, and sheltered from the weather and marauding spring bears, the greenhouse is perfect for them. And there are all

Carpenter ants

those nice, tender seedlings. But to wipe out the colonies is to do violence to tens of thousands individuals. Who has the more just cause, me or them? It is with extreme reluctance that I go to war with them, but I do. They invade my underground house each year also, and I have only two choices; either wipe them out, or leave the premises and allow the structures to disintegrate. You can't live in the same house with them. They run over you at night. They bite. They get into your clothes. They eventually will bring your structures down. My spiritual training tells me that were I more advanced I could eliminate them by thought alone. But I am not that advanced. So I war with them on several fronts year after year.

Poison has never seemed to work on the carpenter ants, at least none that I have found or am willing to use. Initially I heard that bone meal shaken on them would run them out. And it did work. My preferred choice of delivery was to dip a straw into the powdered bone meal and blow it into the tunnels they make in my posts, rafters and beams. But bone meal stinks. And it is probably food for other pests, considering I know of hu-

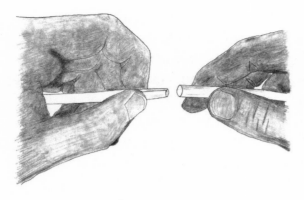

mans who eat the stuff. So I switched to boric acid for a number of years. It is a white powder which, when diluted with water, was used for a century or more in America as eye wash. Now, alas, there are labels on the bottles warning of toxicity. So these days I usually use cayenne red pepper. Drives them nuts to get powdered with that. It may take a couple of weeks of blowing it into their tunnel entrances every three or four days, but it definitely will work. We don't have much in the way of termites here, but I have often wondered if it would do in their colonies too. If the ants' entrances are in a difficult place to reach, I join two or more straws together by increasing the end of one lengthwise, pinching it a little to narrow the circumference and inserting it into the end of a second or third straw.

For a while it was mice which were doing in the seedlings. You could tell by their droppings. For some reason this only lasted for a couple of years and hasn't reoccurred since. I handled the problem in the traditional manner; cats, traps and, finally, poison.

Now about the #@%$&! gophers. I should tell you that my first two greenhouses, the original flatland one and the one attached to the Garden House, were built in really heavy gopher country. They were both built on the same site – the garden house having cannibalized the original greenhouse at the best sun spot on my flatlands. This site is next to an alfalfa field owned by a farmer who regularly sows his field with poisoned oats. Word must get around, for the gophers seem to migrate to my land where the most lethal deterrent is usually something like the Wrigley's Chewing Gum Defense. Unlike the grow hole, which was in close proximity, the original earth-sheltered greenhouse never had gopher problems. I attributed this to the wood and polyethylene barriers that were holding back the earth. The main grow bed was a couple of feet below surface, and I figured that this must be lower than most gophers dug. I suspect I figured wrong. True, they never found their way in, but they would have eventually. I only used that greenhouse for two years before it morphed into the garden house.

The greenhouse part of the garden house was at surface level. When I built it, I sank polyethylene-wrapped boards around the parameter of the grow beds and that seemed to work for a year or so before the %#@$&! gophers found their way in. I later learned that some people have had success with sinking three-foot galvanized wire mesh beneath the surface and bending the last foot away from the area they are trying to protect. This way when the gopher hits the wire mesh and tries to go beneath, he winds up digging in the opposite direction from the area being protected. Turns the #@$%&! fiends right around!

The hillside greenhouse was an interesting study. For the entire first ten-year period, back when the greenhouse was in full production, I never had a gopher problem. I was certain that the depth of the structure kept them out. Then there was about a ten-year period when the greenhouse wasn't much in use. The plastic glazing (Filon) had clouded up and wasn't transmitting enough growth rays to promote a useable crop. But with the Y2K scare, I decided to reglaze and in 1999 was back in production. Or so I thought. The first year back I had a fine greenhouse garden going. Spinach, tomatoes, lettuce, Swiss chard, kale, cabbage and then from somewhere a #@&$%! gopher appeared. I thought he must have fallen in through the unscreened vents above and before he could wipe out too many plants I was able to deal with him. He boldly peeked out of his hole one day and I pounced with a shovel blade which disposed of him permanently. I thought that was the end of it, but the rip-offs continued. I lost that year's crop. I somehow figured that the second gopher must have fallen at the same time and would die from starvation, unable to find a way back to the outside surface.

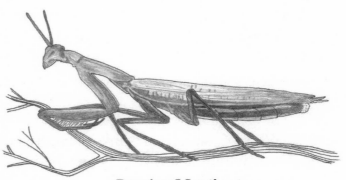

Praying Mantis

Or I figured if it did find a way up, it wouldn't return since the place was absolutely barren due to the fact they had eaten every single bit of greenery there. I figured that if there were tunnels to the outside, they would collapse over the winter and there would be no motivation to return to a barren place. Ah, such naiveté. After the next year's crop and the one after that were up and producing the #@$%&!s struck again and again, wiping everything out.

In the spring of '04 a couple of volunteers showed up and we were able to dig up the four main planting beds and line them below with 1/4-inch galvanized wire mesh. We brought the wire all the way around the beds above ground level eight to twelve inches also. "Won't they climb over that?" once of the volunteers asked. "They're digging critters, not climbing critters," I answered, fairly sure of myself from the experience of my wire-lined, raised carrot bed which has withstood gopher assaults for fifteen years.

Though, in truth, if I discovered they were pole vaulting into the beds, parachuting down, or cutting through the wire with an arc welder, I wouldn't be too surprised. I found nearly thirty years ago that they had dug a direct route through my $500 underground house to its root cellar. You must understand that in that house the flooring is the extraordinary earth carpet floor where we work the earth smooth as finished concrete, lay out a layer of polyethylene and roll out wall to wall carpeting. This results in one of the finest of floors ever — quiet, cheap, easy on the feet and joints. It's like walking on a golf course green. And you don't need to pour a footing, buy and install floor joists, and then put in cross bracing, sub flooring and costly hardwood flooring.

But I was standing on that carpet one day and it gave way beneath my heels, exactly as the earth in your garden gives way when you collapse a gopher run. So I did what I do when this happens in my garden: I started collapsing the run beneath the carpet with my heels to both discourage them and see where the run took me. Where it went was straight to my in-house root cellar. This cellar was bare earth floor and the subterranean scofflaws had surfaced there, chewed through a

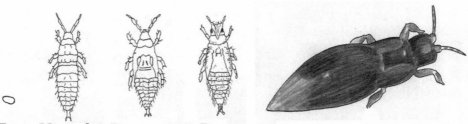

Egg   Nymph   Pro-pupa   Pupa   Adult Greenhouse Thrip

cardboard box and ripped off two-thirds of my winter potato stash.

Shore fly pupae

Boards on the root cellar floor the next year ended any more such gopher adventures. The gopher-run depression in my carpeted floor is there to this day, though I could repair it in an hour by throwing back the polyethylene and carpet, tamping and troweling in some earth from outside, and replacing the plastic and carpet making the problem undetectable. As it is, I keep the run visible as a testament to the ingenuity of the fiends of the furrows.

Shore fly adult

Some of the following is either paraphrased or borrowed outright from an uncopyrighted University of Tennessee Agricultural Extension Service publication #PB 1594 titled *Insect Management in Greenhouses*. It will give you some idea of

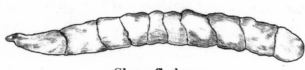

Shore fly larva

what to look for if your greenhouse is infested with insect and mite pests, and some strategies for dealing with them that are more extensive than the few I have used and mentioned, the foremost being a "yellow sticky trap". You will recall these were the round yellow plastic disks smeared with baby oil. There are other commercial traps.

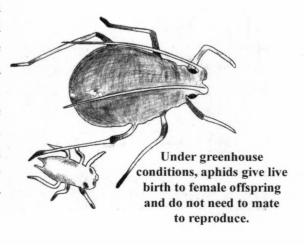

Under greenhouse conditions, aphids give live birth to female offspring and do not need to mate to reproduce.

Lacewing eggs

Hatching larvae crawl down the threads to start feeding on insects.

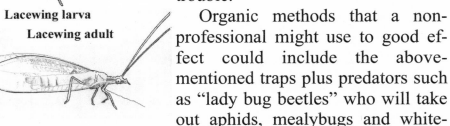

Lacewing larva

Lacewing adult

Though blue ones attract thrips well, the yellow ones "capture a variety of pests including winged aphids, whiteflies, fungus gnats and shore flies." A few pests in a greenhouse can be tolerated. Only time and experience will tell you what the threshold is between acceptable and real trouble.

Organic methods that a non-professional might use to good effect could include the above-mentioned traps plus predators such as "lady bug beetles" who will take out aphids, mealybugs and whiteflies. You can get a package of 1,500 ladybugs for as little as $9.95 from Territorial Seed Company, among others. You can also get praying mantises by mail . Then there are predatory nematodes which are the "only biological control that works below the surface but will not harm plants or earthworms." And there are caterpillar parasites which are "wasps" that kill 200 kinds of caterpillars but won't sting you. And there are spider-mite predators good for five spider mites per day or 20 of their eggs. Finally there are green lacewings which will attack most any soft-bodied insect and will destroy up to 60 aphids or whiteflies per hour.

If traps and

Mealy bugs

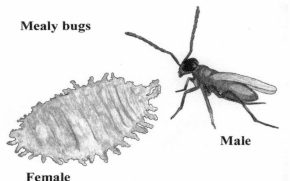

Male

Female

Brown soft scale

Long brown soft scale

Top view

Side view

Hemispherical scale

predators haven't helped your crop, you can always spray. Non toxic organic sprays are sold by Territorial Seed Company, Charlie's Greenhouse & Garden, Park's Seeds, Gaiam Real Goods, R. H. Shumway's and others.

Here's how the University of Tennessee suggests we check for nuisance bugs in the greenhouse:

•Put out traps. One or two 3x5 inch "cards" (traps) per 1,000 sq. ft. of planting area will suffice for testing purposes.

•When scouting for fungus gnat adults, place sticky cards horizontally on pots or on the growing medium surface.

•Use a 10X hand lens to identify insects. These insects are caught on sticky traps:

Whitefly adults
Leafminer adults
Thrips adults
Scale and mealybug adult males
Fungus gnat adults
Winged aphids
Misc. flies (e.g., shore flies and drain flies)
Small bees and wasps

These insects are NOT caught on sticky traps:

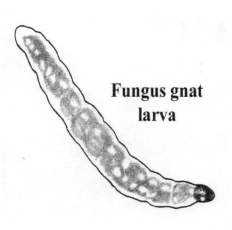

Fungus gnat larva

> Non-winged aphids
> Spider mites
> Mealybug immatures
>   and adult females
> Scale immatures and
>   adult females
> Egg, larva/nymph and
>   pupa stages of many
>   greenhouse pests.

So yellow sticky traps will catch many of the things threatening your greenhouse crops. Though I haven't tried it in my greenhouses yet, I am told that the old-time fly paper works. It is the classic sticky trap. Fly paper was in most homes a century ago and is still in many barns today. It comes coiled up in a little tube and you pull the sticky strip out like a party favor and hang it up. It is yellow. Both feed stores and hardware stores usually carry it.

You should also do manual checks:

•Randomly examine plants

•Pay particular attention to specific plant varieties that are noticeably more susceptible to certain pests.

•Examine leaf undersides, especially young leaves, for all stages of

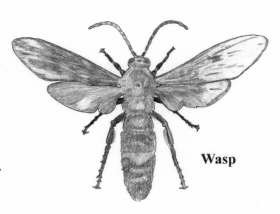

Wasp

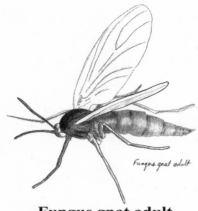

Fungus gnat adult

whiteflies, mealybugs, aphids, spider mites and scales.

- •Examine upper side of leaf for:
  - — Leafminer tunnels
  - — Distortion and discoloration resulting from feeding by thrips, aphids, whiteflies, spider mites, scales, and mealybugs or egglaying damage (leafminers)

- —Honeydew sticky-shiny substance excreted by aphids, soft scales, whiteflies and mealy bugs
- — Sooty mold – dark fungal growth on honeydew
- — Examine terminal growth for immature thrips and aphids
- —Examine the main plant stems for scales and mealy bugs
- — Look at the base of stems, leaves and other protected crevices for mealybug eggs and thrips immatures
- — Examine plant roots for fungus gnat larvae and root mealy bugs.

All right, so you have no idea what fungus gnat larvae, or mealybug eggs or leafminer tunnels look like. Me neither. That's when you go to books like *Garden Insects of North America* by Whitney Cranshaw, or visit websites like www.ipm.ucdavis.edu, which is the official site of the University of California's *Integrated Pest Management Program;* or

Cornell University's Resource Guide for Organic Insect and Disease Management at www.nysaes.cornell.edu/pp/resourceguide: or "Protect Your Garden With Beneficial Bugs" at www.MotherEarthNews.com .

Don't get hysterical if you find sign of a few pests. They are food for the beneficial predators. Pests in moderation are part of the equation. Get hysterical only if they are doing major damage. If your soil is healthy – if it has plenty of organic matter, fertilizer and moisture, and is in the pH range that suits your specific crops — in most cases the pests won't get too far out of control. Put some precautionary fly paper up and monitor it, and do occasional random examinations of the plants. If you find a badly-infected leaf, you can pluck it and drown the critters in a bucket of soapy water. If it's a whole plant that is infested, you can pull it and burn it.

Zip lock your questions into baggies and take it into your county extension agent. If he can't identify it, he'll know who can. Label the baggy and keep it for later years when you have forgotten, or when you can help others with similar problems.

You always have the predators and organic sprays if things get out of hand.

Then there is the question of screening the vents. Myself, I have never found it necessary. Screen costs a little, can be damaged, and may not be suitable for the entire range of critters you may feel you need to exclude. Leafminers, for example, may be excluded with 0.025 inch mesh while western flower thrips require 0.0075 inch mesh. But the big-

Spider mite watching a predator eat its eggs.

gest drawback to screening is that it cuts down on the air flow. This may not be of major importance to commercial growers with their power driven fans, but to the homesteader grower who may not have electricity it could be of paramount importance. You definitely want good circulation on hot, sunny days.

The only thing I have screened for is gophers. As described, I have begun lining all my growing beds with quarter-inch galvanized wire mesh. I bring it eight or more inches above ground. I suspect it should work equally well for voles and moles and probably any other "large" burrowing critters. So far, at least, it has worked well for me. Knock on wood.

The U. of Tennessee Agricultural Extension Service publication on page 102 and much of the material from page 103 through 106 was developed by Frank A. Hale, Professor, Entomology and Plant Pathology Agricultural Extension Service, University of Tennessee, and Raymond A. Cloyd, Assistant Professor, Extension Entomologist, University of Illinois. It was originally developed by Elizabeth Will, Graduate Student, James Faust, former Assistant Professor, Ornamental Horticulture and Landscape Design, and Frank A. Hale, Assistant Professor, Entomology and Plant Pathology.

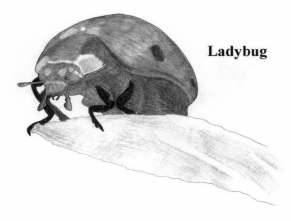

Ladybug

CHAPTER 12
Rabbits and other beneficial critters

Some years ago there was a flurry of excitement among the counter-culture homesteaders about the benefits of having rabbits or other domestic animals in the greenhouse on a more or less permanent basis. The benefits are great in such an arrangement. For starters, and perhaps most important, the rabbits generate carbon dioxide which is usually in short supply in the plant-heavy, enclosed greenhouse atmosphere. A second benefit is that rabbit bodies generate heat in cold weather to help warm the place. Then, too, they turn plant scraps into soil-enhancing manure. There was talk (which I haven't heard since) that the ammonia contained in their waste was beneficial to plants in gas form. Rabbits may be sold and can become an important cash crop for struggling homesteader families. Or they can be cuddly little pets. And of course — for those so inclined — they produce meat, and fur skins for warm clothing. Finally, there is the auxiliary benefit of needing less rabbit feed in the winter since they are partially warmed by the greenhouse atmosphere itself and need metabolize less to maintain body temperature.

This obvious symbiotic relationship between rabbits and greenhouse plants was much discussed in the heydays of the hippy back-too-the-land movement in the late 1960's and '70s. Why it never became common practice was a puzzle to me for years. Then recently, while doing research I came across this statement in Delores Wolfe's book *Growing Food in Solar Greenhouses*.

" 'Rabbits *do not belong in the greenhouse!*' Those were the first words our friend and rabbit-raiser, Charles Sheaff, said to us when we asked him about it. Rabbits can not tolerate the temperatures of the greenhouse on bright sunny days — even in January. You never see rabbits gamboling in a field on hot days. They stay in their earth-cooled underground quarters, venturing outside only in the cool of the evening or early morning."

This is a compelling argument except for one factor —

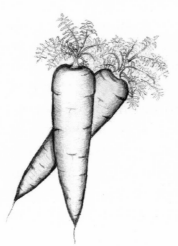

it doesn't apply to our earth-sheltered greenhouses. We have the *cold-sink,* remember, which is a great environment for rabbits. Your cold-sink is going to stay cool on even the hottest of days, perhaps as much as thirty degrees cooler than other parts of the greenhouse. If you want to be absolutely sure of this, put strips of carpeting or other insulation you can tread upon down on the walkway over the rabbit area. Your rabbits will be virtually guaranteed comfort on even the hottest of days. And, of course, on those freezing January nights they are equally comfortable snug as they are down in the warmth of the earth, their natural environment. Rabbits belong in *good* greenhouses, you bet!

It has upset me for many years to see rabbits kept in cages above ground year around in sheds or barns or beneath trees to roast in the summer and freeze in the winter. This was bad enough when people had hutches for them with roofs and partial flooring and siding. But to see them in nothing but wire cages seems to me extremely cruel. They are bedding down on — in fact spending their whole lives on — a mesh of steel bars. It may look like wire mesh to humans but to them it is steel bars. It is the equivalent of human beings having to spend their lives sleeping on half or one inch steel bars in a mesh four inches apart. And without any sort of bedding. Just steel bars to lie, sit and walk barefoot upon.

When I have brought this up with rabbit breeders and ask why they don't throw in some straw for them to bed down on, I am told that they eat the straw. When I ask why they don't put a bit of board that they can sleep on, I am told that they foul the boards. The wire mesh is necessary for sanitation, I am told. This has necessitated deep thought on my part, for my next greenhouse, my super greenhouse, will certainly have rabbit tenants.

At this point in time I am planning to have the rabbits in a communal area in the cold-sink until I can ascertain how severe the problems are. There are bullies, rapes, unwanted pregnancies and the killing of some of the young. I acknowledge that some of the rabbits will have to be segregated into cages for at least part of the time. But I think I am going to deal with the problem of the bars they must sleep on by spreading an inch or so of earth on the bottom bars as the cage rests on the earthen floor. To clean the cage I will raise it, letting the fouled earth fall below through the mesh where I'll shovel it up for the compost pile or earth worm bin. When I replace the cage, I'll again sprinkle an inch or so of soft earth on the lower mesh.

If I do indeed have some of the rabbits uncaged on the floor of the cold-sink, might they chew on the wooden sides or try to tunnel up to freedom? I'll watch that closely, too, and if it looks like trouble I'll line the sides with mesh and the bottom maybe six or so inches under the earthen floor. An alternative might be a solid concrete floor that can be swept up and

mopped from time to time. In any event I'm going to experiment with plastic tubes they can crawl up through to get to an enclosed outside area so they can gambol in the morning and evening sun.

But is this environment good for the rabbits? Here's some research I pulled off the Internet. The Finica Ecologica, University of Agriculture and Forestry, Ho Chi Minh City, ran an experiment with 30 small scale farmers at its Goat and Rabbit Research Center, Sontay, in two North Vietnam provinces from January until July 1996 in order to answer this very question. The results were impressive:

"All the performance parameters were significantly improved in rabbits housed in the underground shelters compared with the (raised) cages. The does in underground shelters were 8% heavier after 2 months in the experiment, they gave birth to 39% more offspring and weaned 60% more than those in cages...

"Rabbit breeding is practiced in almost all developing countries and contributes to family nutrition and economy, through the availability of a source of animal protein, as well as through extra income by sale of animals. Rabbit production has been developed in Vietnam based on the conventional system of cages raised above the ground. The major constraints of this housing system are low reproduction due to high temperatures in summer (30-35 degree Centigrade/86-96 degree Fahrenheit) and high mortality of the offspring due to cold 12-15 Centigrade/53.6-59 Fahrenheit) and wet weather in the winter ... high temperature affects spermatogenesis, reducing the volume and concentration of ejaculates and also affects sperm mobility after 8 hours at 36 C/96.8 F (or 14 days at 30C/86 F). High temperature also affects growing rabbits negatively due to reduced rates of live weight gain caused by the reduction of feed intake."

You bet rabbits belong in greenhouses. In *good* greenhouses they do.

The carbon dioxide (CO_2) benefits of animals, especially rabbits, in a greenhouse can be spectacular. Ace researcher David Fairall dug a book out of a library for me called *"The Hydroponic Hot House; Low-Cost, High-Yield Greenhouse Gardening"* by James B. DeKorne, who one suspects was a 1960's hippy and 1970's hippy, back-to-the-land homesteader. Despite the fact that parts are dated, and there are one or two obvious mistakes, this is a really fine, useful book.

Obvious from the title, DeKorne's primary focus is on hydroponic gardening, which he is quite enthusiastic about. But in the spirit of a true pioneer he dabbled with many other aspects of greenhouse design and food production. Glory be, his was a pit greenhouse, four feet deep, with earth bermed against the north wall. And he built his at the exact same time I was messing with my growholes and first earth - sheltered greenhouse.  True, he hadn't stumbled across the cold-sink, but he was experimenting in a lot of ways I wasn't.

And one of those experiments was rabbits in the greenhouse. Because the rabbits were on the cool, four-foot-deep floor, and protected from the sun by solution-filled hydroponic tanks above, they never envinced any heat stress that he could detect. If they had, DeKorne notes, he could have moved them to a cooler spot (had one existed).

DeKorne probably doesn't have any more empirical evidence than I do, seeing as he seems to have never received a grant either, or had teams of scientists collecting data on his work, but he does present some convincing photos comparing crop yields when they were CO_2 enriched by his rabbits and when they were not. He quotes a National Fertilizer Association 1949 publication "Hunger Signs in Crops" which states, "The air contains only about 300 parts per million of carbon dioxide. Thus vast volumes of air must be worked over by plants in order to obtain enough carbon in the form of carbon dioxide. In fact if the air were richer in this substance, plants could grow faster and bigger than they do now."

How much faster? Homeharvest.com states tests at Colorado State University reveal that at 220 parts per million of CO_2 "a slow-down in plant growth is significantly noticeable" while below 150 ppm "most plants stop growing." On the other hand CO_2 at 550 ppm increased the production of bibb lettuce by 40%, carnations 30%, roses by 39.7% and tomatoes 29% over the normal growth rate at 300 ppm.

DeKorne estimates his rabbits raised his greenhouse CO_2 to 700 ppm to 800 ppm, and says that professional growers jack their greenhouse levels up to one-thousand to two-thousand parts per million. They do that with special liquid butane or natural gas stoves rather than traditional, integrated farming techniques such as we are discussing here.

DeKorne writes: "Michael Saxton of Harvard University, the man who first informed me of this important subject states that:

"To some extent carbon dioxide can make up for lack of light. An experiment with cucumbers shows this:

```
60% shade ..........................64% yield
Full sunlight ....................100% yield
60% shade + CO₂ ...............92% yield
Full sunlight + CO₂ .............147% yield
```

"The added carbon dioxide is almost enough to make up for the 60% shade."

Fowl may also form a symbiotic relationship with your hothouse greenery. Just like rabbits they add body heat, carbon dioxide, eat up scraps and contribute manure fertilizer. They make delicious Sunday dinners and you can't beat fresh eggs for breakfast. But in certain circumstances also, you may be able to let them free among the greenhouse plants for both insect and weed control.

The most respected weeders are geese. In some parts of the world for some crops they are the primary weeding agents. With their long necks they can get in and weed around plants where mechanized weeders and hoes can't reach. They do not impact the soil like heavy machinery. They can work in rain-drenched or swampy areas without getting bogged down. They do not deplete costly oil resources. Their exhausts fertilize the soil rather than polluting the air, destroying the protective ozone layer and causing global warming.

Geese have the helpful characteristic of loving most grasses but aversion to broadleaf plants. They are of particular use in fields of monocrops such as cotton, tobacco, potatoes, cane berries, sugar beets, garlic, onions, carrots, hops, blueberries, mint and other herbs. They are also excellent in orchards, and in fields of evergreen and deciduous nursery crops. The hang-up is that they have to be fenced in usually, which can be expensive even with portable fences (labor). In the family garden with its variety of crops they may wipe out plants you are trying to nurture. And experience from childhood tells me that they can be ornery. I remember us kids shrinking back to the protection of adults when a hissing, wing-flapping goose charged, and being warned that those wings were powerful enough to break a kid's arm. It was probably a gander charging. The reader must be aware that the males of most species, if not "fixed", can be overtly aggressive — the stallion, the bull, the boar, the beer-soaked redneck. You might want to stick with the females.

Since the greenhouse is enclosed, your fencing problem is automatically solved. There is, however, the problem of diversity of crops. Unless you are monocropping, or just have a few varieties that geese specifically don't like, you may wind up with the problem that family gardeners have with the geese taking out beneficial plants. As weeders they might do best in large, professional monocropping greenhouses — one devoted solely to tomatoes, for example.

Geese are vegetarians and as such won't eat up bugs, snails and slugs. Ducks will, though, and one or two could be a big help. Though I have never kept them myself, I believe I will after reading Eliot Coleman's book *Four Season Harvest*. I can only wish that someday someone might write as nice things about me as Coleman does about ducks. Listen:

> "We are long-time fans of the duck. We
> keep three or four of them as companions and
> helpers in our yard. Over the years we have
> raised several breeds: Australian Spotted Ban-
> tams, Welsh Harlequins, and Indian Runners.
> Each breed has virtues and it is difficult to
> recommend one over the other. Ducks are the
> perfect backyard livestock because they are
> so well behaved. Ducks need water only
> for drinking not swimming, although they do
> appreciate the water from a sprinkler in
> hot, dry weather, just as the garden does.
> They don't scratch and fight like chickens do,
> they aren't noisy like chickens are, and they
> lay their eggs at night so the basis for a
> fresh omelet awaits us most every morning
> when we let them out of their night shelter.
> They lay more eggs than chickens and the eggs
> are richer and better tasting. Best of all ducks
> lay eggs at a reasonable rate in the winter with-
> out fancy housing or supplementary light. Even
> if fed on a homegrown diet of garden and kitchen
> scraps instead of the expensive mixed feeds
> that chickens require, ducks will lay at about
> 60 percent of the summer rate."

Coleman recommends ducks as "highly effective pest

control" who "take care of the slug problem with almost magical efficiency." Ducks aren't perfect, mind you. They must be fenced out of spring gardens and greenhouses when plants are sprouting. "But considering the larger picture, any minor damage they do is insignificant compared with the benefits they provide and the delight we take in their company. Friendly, curious, and often hilariously ridiculous, they possess enough dignified reserve that they never become bothersome." In short, says Coleman, ducks "provide a daily source of fresh eggs, devastatingly effective bug and slug control, and charming garden companionship."

I'm sold, Ducks it'll be.

Chickens are another matter. Yes, they will eat nearly any bug they come across, but they will also devastate much of your garden. Don't even let them *think* about a patch with ripe, red strawberries. And watch out with them in among the tomatoes. In fact my last flock of seven chickens totally wiped out the vegetation in their 15' x 45' pen, except for a couple of clumps of the noxious weed tansy which I pulled up myself. They'd be fine for CO_2, body heat, manure, and eggs in your greenhouse, though. And you might want to take this tip: no matter what fowl you keep, Pavlovize them. That is, make Pavlov's chickens (duck, geese) out of them. It's actually quite easy. Whenever you feed them bang on something just before setting down the food. In my chicken pen I keep an old, empty two-gallon oil can for this use. I bang on it with my knuckles for about thirty seconds. In a month's time they are so trained they come running to me from wherever they are in the neighborhood. I effortlessly gather and lead them back into their pen like the Pied Piper.

Now about critter housing in your greenhouse. We've already established that the cold-sink is a splendid environment for rabbits. But how do you get down to them if there is that walkway above? Simple. You either nail the boards together (or use plywood) and hinge them so they fold up flat against the wall, giving you access to the pit below, or you lay the boards unnailed on top of their supports and pick them up and stack them whenever you want to drop below. The one thing you must not do with either method, however, is remove the support they rest on, for the supports are what keeps the posts in the P/S/P system from pushing in from the pressure of the earth outside. The supports do double duty. Will you have to climb over them to get from one part of the cold-sink to another while tending the rabbits? Yes, you will. Life is not easy on the frontier.

There is yet another critter which seems a good greenhouse companion — fish. Like rabbits, this concept created a buzz in the late 60's and 1970's. Fish farming in a greenhouse

sure seems promising when you first think of it. The mass of water in the fish tanks serve as heat sinks gradually warming in the day and radiating heat out at night. Passive heat gain while generating protein! Fish are remarkable little protein factories. Since they require no energy to support themselves in the water, floating as they do, and since they are cold-blooded and thus require little energy to keep warm, they can utilize more of their food for body mass. As stated in an editorial in Rodale's *Organic Gardening and Farming Magazine* in April 1971, "Almost 90 percent of the food given to beef cattle, for example, is 'wasted' because it is used to keep up the animal's body temperature. The harvest of protein food in the form of meat is small in return for the corn, grain and hay that is invested in supporting the animals." But not so with fish.

(Sigh) I wish I could report favorably in the greenhouse/ fish farming concept, but, alas, I cannot. We were all jacked up with enthusiasm in the early '70s with the optimistic projections coming out of the New Alchemy Institute regarding this. But their experiments did not seem to work out and they finally conceded, "Costs associated with indoor, freshwater aquaculture today are simply too high to justify a continued emphasis on this subject."

Our man James DeKorne gave greenhouse aquaculture a real try, and devotes more than seventeen pages to it in his book. In almost every way, his fish experiments were disappointing. The energy demands of aerating and circulating the water and the voracious feeding demands of the fish were only two of the problems. Obvious symbiotic relations such as using the stale fish water as fertilizer for plants didn't work well. Though the seedlings seemed to thrive on it, the mature plants did poorly. But you've got to give the guy an "A" for effort and ingenuity. Faced with a feed problem he began opening the doors and windows of his greenhouse on summer nights and hung a twelve-volt tail-light-bulb over the fish tank to

draw in the flying insects which were greatly enjoyed by the fish waiting in a circle beneath the bulb. Numerous insect parts such as wings floating on the surface each morning testified to the efficacy of this system. But summer is only three months a year, and the fish have to be fed the other nine months too. Though some have suggested raising aquarium fish for sale at pet stores as a possible winner, I think I will close the book on greenhouse aquaculture until I learn of some other pioneer who has made it work.

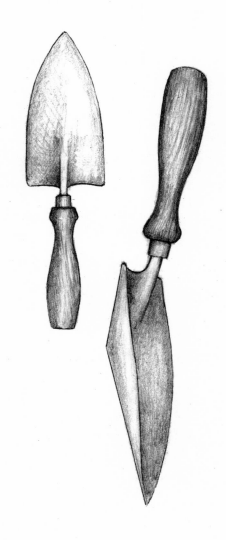

CHAPTER 13
Growing tips

Greenhouse microclimates

All greenhouses have microclimates within. It's to your advantage to learn where and what they are, and to utilize them. Some plants like full sunlight, others appreciate considerable shade. Plants such as peppers won't even set fruit below 65 degrees while others, such as spinach, thrive in the 40 to 50 degree range. If you are serious about producing abundantly, it would pay you to learn how the microclimate varies in your unit and at what times of the day and season.

The way to do this of course is with thermometers. You will want the maximum/minimum thermometers, which will measure both the highest and lowest temperatures and record them till you reset them. If you place the thermometers in specific spots, one in a presumed cool area and one in a warm area, and if you do this in various places throughout the structure in various seasons and weather conditions, and if you record your findings, you will get a picture of your greenhouse's microclimates. You will have a much clearer picture then of where to site your various plants. Remember that sensitive ones like tomatoes may be planted in movable containers and hung, for example, from the central glazing rafter in the cooler hours and placed in cooler shaded areas in

the heat of a summer scorcher. Portable planters also make it handy to bring cold-sensitive plants into the house to be placed before a large southern window in the wintertime.

Other thermometers are designed to measure the temperature of the soil. Temperature there, surprisingly important for mature plants, is of paramount importance when the seeds are germinating. There are commercial heating elements designed to specifically heat the soil, though starting trays on top of your thermal barrels should do most jobs admirably. And again, the starting trays may be brought into the house when conditions require.

Those really into it might want to make records of the humidity in the greenhouse. Too little humidity and the plant leaves will feel dry and the plants won't have vigor. During a prolonged period of low humidity they may wilt and go to seed early. Above 70 percent, humidity encourages the spread of damping-off and other mold diseases. It may also encourage leaf growth over fruit. Sixty percent relative humidity seems to be the optimum for a greenhouse. A humidistat can turn on and off a humidifier to keep the humidity at a desired level if you are wealthy or a professional grower. Otherwise, a wet/dry bulb thermometer is much less costly and will allow you to calculate the humidity and manually manipulate it with ventilation, pans of water, wet cloths and the like. Ask at your hardware or garden supply store for a wet/dry thermometer.

And then there is the question of natural light within the greenhouse. Some areas are going to get considerably more shade than others – those near the east and west walls, and those shaded by plants or planters and other objects. Some are going to bask in a great deal of sunlight. Then there is the question of how much light will penetrate the glazing at different times of the day and year. The closer to perpendicular the rays are striking the glazing, the better the penetration. Unless you are a pro, or a fanatic with a light densitometer, or have a friend you could borrow one from, you are going to have to take visual observations of when and where the shadows fall. And you should calculate by sight or science how far off from perpendicular your rays are striking the glazing, and where those rays are striking the glazing, and where those rays are landing in the greenhouse. If the pitch of your glazing differs in two or more sections, in different places the greenhouse will be getting different intensities of light which may change according to the time of day. The intensities unquestionably will change by season. Observation, experimentation and experience are your best guides here.

The effects of shading may be mitigated some by sitting the low-growing plants like lettuce on the south parts of the beds, medium height plants like Swiss chard in the center and higher plants like

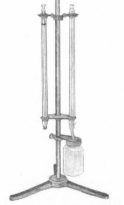

One type of wet/dry thermometer

kale and tomatoes on the north side. There should be a walk-way then before your water-filled barrels, and in the warmer six months you may utilize some of that space by putting a bench next to the barrels and putting plants in containers on them. In the colder six months, depending on where you live you, will likely want to dismantle that bench and move the plants to allow the barrels to absorb as much of the sun's warmth as possible. The top of the barrels affords a great growing surface year around of course. From the top of the barrels to the glazing above should be pretty consistently the warmest area in the greenhouse.

Greenhouse soils

Soils used in the greenhouse should be lighter than outdoor garden soils. This is because the high degree of irrigation needed inside tends to compact the earth more than outside garden beds drawing on the more abundant deep moisture. Lighter soil means more humus. For this reason, too, one should tend more to sandy soils rather than those heavy with clay. A classic greenhouse soil might be 1 part good garden soil with compost, 1 part sorghum moss and 1 part sand (or perlite.) You enrich this with various organic minerals and fertilizers to suit the taste of the individual crops.

Good gardeners check soil acidity, with pH 7 being neu-tral. Those in the know recommend pH 5 to 6.5 for the green-house. It is the amount of calcium in the soil available to plants which determines the acidity. To get it more alkaline add calcium in the form of lime.

Nitrogen, that classic plant nutrient, may be added organically in the form of fish and seaweed emulsions, chopped plants (healthy ones), blood and bone meals and, of course, well-rotted manures or manure teas. These also add trace minerals.

Phosphorus and potassium both contribute to your plant's abilities to resist disease, sort of the way Echinacea and goldenseal root boost the immune system in humans. Plants which stop growing and developing, and which may have stems and leaves turning red or purple, are signs of possible phosphorus deficiency. If the leaves show yellow streaking and/or spotting it may mean potassium deficiencies. Dig up one of those plants. Poorly-developed root systems are a sign of potassium deficiency.

There is a big controversy about sterilizing greenhouse soils to kill organisms possibly harmful to your plants. I have never used such soil unless the potting soils I bought in the dead of the winter happened to be sterilized. Live soil seems to me the best way to go. A possible exception might be soil used for the germination of seedlings.

Companion Planting

Some plant types get along as well together as Americans and Canadians used to, and some dislike each other like Israelis and displaced Palestinians. Wise gardeners find out which is which, for companionable plants can help each other grow and help each other repel pests. Incompatible species can actually hinder growth and can even sick pests on their neighbors.

Here are some of the preferences of common greenhouse plants:

Tomatoes and all members of the Brassica family feud. Keep them apart. Though tomatoes get along well with chives, onions, garlic, carrots, parsley and asparagus, they are prejudiced against potatoes and fennel. Fennel doesn't seem to get along with anybody, in fact, so keep it out of your greenhouse.

The Brassicas are the cabbage family, which includes not only the cabbages but cauliflower, broccoli, collards, Brussels sprouts, kohlrabi and, surprisingly, turnips and ruta-baga. Many of these are hardy and will winter over well in your earth-sheltered greenhouse. They are good companions with the aromatic plants like rosemary, sage, dill, celery, chamomile and the mints. Though they do okay with bush beans, they should not be planted with pole beans. They do like potatoes, onions, and beets, though these three do so well outside, and root cellar so well, you may want to keep them out there rather than in the limited greenhouse space. Exceptions to this suggestion might be growing a few onions as insect repelling companions, or a few beets for their greens.

Spinach is kind of anti-social but does well with strawberries. Strawberries also like bush beans and lettuce. Lettuce likes bush beans, too, plus pole beans, radishes, and carrots. Parsley tends to be grumpy and does best with just toma-toes.

The gardening tips offered here are not the final word. Don't become discouraged by their seeming complexity. You may still have a fine greenhouse garden without following them. Yet, in all likelihood, if you can work them into your greenhouse over the years you will be rewarded.

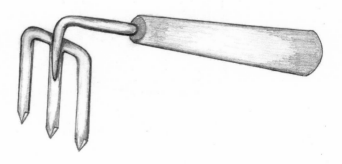

134

CHAPTER 14
Root cellars

"I dug my cellar in the side of a hill sloping to the south, where a woodchuck formerly dug his burrow, down through sumac and blackberry roots and the lowest stain of vegetation, six feet square by seven feet deep to a fine sand where pota- toes would not freeze in any weather ... I took particular pleas- ure in this breaking of the ground, for in almost all latitudes men dug into the earth for an equable temperature, where they store their roots as of old, and long after the superstructure had disappeared posterity remark its dent in the earth." – Henry David Thoreau in *Walden*

Root cellars go hand in hand with earth-sheltered green- houses. The two structures have several characteristics in common. The most obvious is that they are both built into the ground. Both utilize the earth's temperature for warmth in the winter and for cooling in the summer. Both allow your family to eat the most nourishing organic foods when the wind is howling and the snow falling. Each can operate independent of commercial electricity and fossil fuels and so are not only environmentally benign and cheap to operate, but also immune to such civilized disruptions as power blackouts. Being earth-sheltered, they are similarly resistant to natural and man-made catastrophes such as tornadoes, hurricanes, conflagration and atomic fallout. But a root cellar has this unique advantage over a greenhouse: in time of crisis it might serve to shelter your family for hours, days or even weeks.

Earth-sheltered greenhouses and root cellars complement but do not duplicate each other. Each has its specific use. The greenhouse will allow you to harvest and immediately enjoy greens like chard and lettuce and kale and such luxuries as

 vine- ripened tomatoes and perhaps even everbearing strawberries. This when the snow is falling and the wind howling. But the root cellar will provide you with year-round bulk food that requires too much growing space to be economically produced in the greenhouse, food that can be grown to maturity within your growing region and then stored in quantities for a number of months with little or no loss of quality.

The principle of root cellaring is simplicity itself: keep food – particularly root crops – cool, humid and in the dark. This can be as simple as: (1) digging a hole in the ground, (2) putting the storable food in a container or structure of some sort and (3) burying it. Most folks envision root cellars as quaint little, picturesque 6'x6' or 6'x8' rock structures dug into a hillside. And indeed that was perhaps the most common form of root cellar throughout most of our nation's history.

But if you accept the definition of Mike and Nancy Bubel, authors of the bible on the subject, *ROOT CELLARING: Natural Cold Storage of Fruits and Vegetables,* you don't even necessarily need a container or structure. They devote an impressive amount of space to the feasibility of preserving crops such as carrots right in the row for several months after the first freeze. They suggest putting down some mouse deterrent such as screening or hardware cloth directly over the tops of the carrots in the row then putting on eight or more inches of mulch. The rows should be staked at the ends so they may be found and dug in the snow. I've had friends tell me they have recovered edible carrots clear into the spring by this method, though, ha ha, it would surely never work on land like mine.

The reason it would never work on my land is because of those fiends of the furrow, the #%$*&! gophers. Other areas are plagued by moles and voles. My area has those pocket gophers who are so diabolically intelligent they are all in Mensa. Ha ha, you think I'm exaggerating, do you? Here's what happened several years after I declared all-out war on them.

I had five thirty-foot rows of delicious, sweet-tasting carrots just coming into their own – the biggest ones were about the size of my little finger, sweet and tender. They were so tasty it was hard for a guy not to thin out too many: in another month they would have six or eight times the bulk, and it was going to be a fine crop which would last me all winter in my root cellar. But one morning when I reached my garden an entire row was gone – every single carrot in the row! It had happened in a single night.

Now, I had been battling the #$%@&! gophers long enough to know their work when I saw it. In fact, I had been in combat with them already that year ever since I saw my lettuce and radishes were taking hits. I had my usual defenses in play. I had empty quart beer bottles buried halfway into the earth every ten feet so that the wind catching them would make them hum and repel gophers like eighty-year-olds reeling back from heavy metal, or rap. I had been flooding the gopher holes for hours, sometimes all night with the garden hose to hopefully drown them out, or at least make their environment miserable.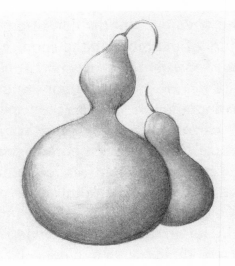

I had rolled moth balls into some of the dry runs to gas them, but as usual they just rolled them back out. I do not poison them because I do not care to have permanent poison in the soils where my food is raised. I hadn't heard of the Wrigley's Chewing Gun defense yet, but it didn't work for me anyway when I tried it.

But I did have a gopher trap.

Yes, friends, a gopher trap. Note that most of the methods of gopher combat reported above are relatively non-violent. But not so a gopher trap. When successful as intended, it pierces the furry little critter through the body from the sides with long spikes. Sometimes it doesn't get them squarely. Sometimes they don't die soon. Sometimes a guy can't check his traps every day. Sometimes they live in unbearable pain for hours or days, which must seem like weeks or months to them.

But I used it anyway. That was the summer a beautiful college student was living on my land. She was an animal activist, a member of People for Ethical Treatment of Animals, PETA, whose wistful hope was to run an animal shelter in the country somewhere. She was working in a local tree nursery at the time, plus caring for her two dogs, two cats and a ferret, and cooking for us all. She was expecting to leave in weeks. She had little time or interest in the garden. She would never know about the trap.

When you set a gopher trap, you put it on a chain on a stake so the gopher can't drag it off. You set it down in his run near the opening. The mound of earth he shoves ahead of him out of the burrow trips the trap. You hope he will die soon. This time he didn't. This time I couldn't get back to the garden for three days and when I did, he was speared through the hip and had crawled out of the burrow to try to free himself. He had worn a circle around the stake in the earth an inch deep. A circle of agony. To put him out of his agony as quickly and as humanely as possible, I grabbed a bucket of water and lowered him in, dangling from the trap at the end of the chain. He did not go willingly. He was protesting. "Set

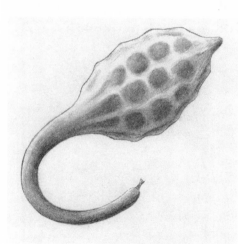

me loose. I won't come back. Haven't you done enough to me already? I've got a wife and kids to support." He took far longer to drown than I had anticipated.

The whole incident disturbed me greatly, and in atonement I confessed it to Ellen. She took it well, with a smile even, "Have you learned your lesson?"

"Yes."

And I have not used a gopher trap since.

But we haven't gotten to the crux of this story. The other gophers cleaned out the rest of the carrots, of course. In just four days they wiped out 150 feet of carrots. Later in that same season I was digging into a pile of excavated earth to add to the roof of the underground "Garden House" when I uncovered what had to be their main stash. It was a cavern they had hollowed out of that soft earth and had filled with my baby carrots. There must have been three quarters of a bushel of carrots there. I stood sadly looking at that scene trying to decide what to do about it. The stash was a hundred feet from the planting beds. They must have dug a hundred-foot tunnel through the hard earth, had excavated a cavern maybe fifty times the size of any single gopher, had done all of that manually, had systematically wiped out five rows of crop, and had hauled the hundreds of carrots there one at a time – no probably two or three at a time, given their diabolical intelligence – had hauled those carrots the gopher distance of a quarter mile. Perhaps they'd had to walk backwards to do it too, that or trip over the carrots dangling the length of their bodies. The @#$ %&! gophers had constructed an entire highway system, excavated a vast cavern which was in fact a root cellar proportionately a dozen times the size of mine. They had done this with-

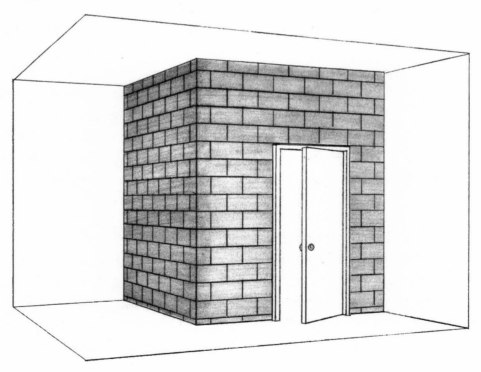

out tools of any sort. And they had done all of this despite the cruel torture and death of one of their own.

I stood staring for some minutes at their root cellar, laden with the bounty of my garden. The carrots were pretty small and would not be particularly rewarding to try to salvage. And the gopher folks had shown exemplary industry and intelligence and sacrifice for the crop. With a sigh I began covering it back up, even adding some extra inches of earth on top for better protection. They had put so much work into it. Such initiative and industry should be rewarded. It is the American way.

Now, if gophers can construct a root cellar, you can too. It can be as simple as my first one which was nothing more than a galvanized garbage can buried in the floor of my original $50 underground house. I remember with pleasure the look of astonishment on the face of George Eddy, an old-timer neighbor, when I handed him a 52-degree beer from the bottom of that can on a 90-degree day in my electricity-free house.

Or a root cellar can be as simple as walling off a corner of your basement with concrete blocks and a metal door (to keep the mice out.) Or you could wall off a part of the basement with painted lumber and riged insulation and put the stored produce in covered plastic pails. If you do build a basement root cellar,

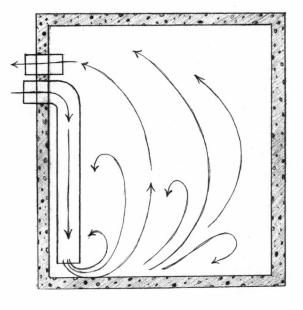

take care to provide ventilation. The illustration on the previous page shows one example. The principle is cool air comes in below and warmer air exits above.

Other ways are to sink a barrel or old freezer or non-

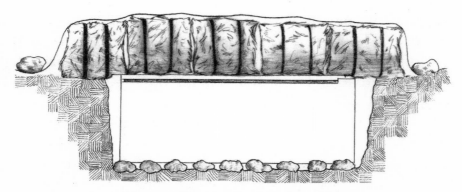

Deep freezer root cellar

working refrigerator on its back into the earth, perhaps against the wall of your house (which wall may depend upon your climate) and cover it with a foot or two of straw for insulation covered with a tarp for moisture.

Or you can build an old timey, new timey, genuine stand-alone root cellar. This makes sense if you don't have a basement to work with and have a number of people to provide for. It also makes sense if you are in hurricane or tornado country, or if there is chance of massive fire or nuclear fallout. They are great shelters.

The principle here is this: Dig into the earth. Build walls and shoring. Waterproof them. Provide for drainage. Provide for ventilation. Put in an insulated door or, better, two insulated doors for an air lock. Backfill with three foot of earth on the roof.

There are thousands of variations to the principles described above. What works best for your climate and micro-climate is impossible to say from here. The best thing to do is find out who in your area has root cellars. Give the folks a call and ask if you can see the cellar and how well it works. They will likely share their knowledge. Country folks are usually quite friendly that way, unless for some reason they have been swamped by requests. You can find them by asking around, advertising in the local paper, putting up signs on bulletin boards or perhaps asking your county extension agent who might have root cellars in your county. For an eye-opening variety of root cellar ideas consult the Bubel's book.

STORAGE

The three things that all root-cellar-stored vegetables and fruits need are cool to cold (but not freezing) temperatures, reasonable humidity and darkness.

The most common root-cellar-stored items are potatoes, apples and carrots. Potatoes are stored by professionals these days in wooden crates they can handle with fork lifts, but you can use smaller wooden boxes with gaps between the slats, or plastic bags you can buy at feed stores, or in four and five-gallon plastic pails with either the lids off, or ventilation holes drilled around the sides. Small holes. Rats can elongate their bodies so that they can worm through a hole the size of a quarter. Mice must be even worse. Ideally potatoes should be stored at 32-40 degrees with 80-90% humidity. But don't get hung up on that. Most root cellars will store your bounty admirably. If it looks like the cellar will freeze during a cold spell, close off the vents and put a shaded, lit kerosene lantern or some other form of mild heating in there nights. Check temperatures often the first year to see how your cellar performs.

Potatoes for storage should not be harvested until their above-ground green parts have been killed by frost. This

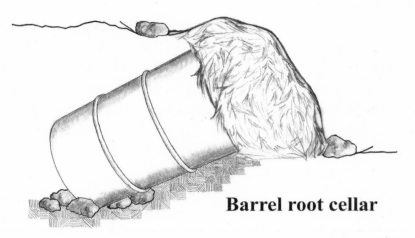

Barrel root cellar

causes a chemical change in the potato which will add to their storage life. Right there you are up on the non-organic commercial growers. Those folks usually spray their potato fields in the fall rather than wait for the frost. This is to meet processing schedules. Then, of course, they coat the potatoes with chemicals which will slow the eyeing, and then pump on more chemicals which will inhibit fungus. This is on top of the pesticides and other chemicals they spray on the green plants and the herbicides and chemical fertilizers they put on the earth. Aren't you glad you're an organic gardener?

Carrots may be stored in sacks, or, if you find that they get limp in your root cellar, in pails of damp sand. If they get limp (and if other crops are shriveling) your cellar probably doesn't have enough humidity. Some folks sop water on the walls and floor to remedy this.

Some refer to apples as the queen of the root-cellared fruit. You want apples that ripen in the fall, particularly those that have the best local reputation for wintering-over well. Then you should be able to eat them late into the spring. Even summer apples will last a month or two in the cellar. Experiment. Though I haven't seen it in the books I've been researching, many folks in my part of the country advise harvesting storage apples only after the first good frost.

Apples have a sullied reputation for storage with other items, particularly with potatoes. The ethylene gas they emit can make potatoes sprout early. But I am assured by experts that if you keep the potatoes and carrots well-separated and have adequate ventilation in the root cellar, you will have little problem. I've usually handled the situation by keeping the apples in plastic pails and taking them out of the cellar periodically to open the lid to let the gas escape and let the apples dry on the surface. I check for any rotting apples then, too. A number of fruits seem to emit ethylene gas — tomatoes for one — but apples seem to emit more than most. You can, in fact, hasten the ripening of green tomatoes by putting apples in among them.

Here are some of the Bubel's storage dos and don'ts, paraphrased, and a few of my own:

> Keep produce in small rather than
>   large piles.
> Don't put them on a bare concrete
>   floor but in raised containers
>   several inches off floor for air
>   circulation.
> Handle produce carefully. Store
>   only the best non-insect dam
>   aged, unbruised and mature pro
>   duce.
> Check stored food often and cull
>   the questionable stuff.
> Harvest storage foods in cold, dry-
>   soil weather.
> Keep vegetables as cool as possible
>   between harvest and storage.
> Make sure your storage space has

adequate ventilation.

Cut leafy tops of root vegetables to within an inch of
the crown and then use those greens.

Don't wash root vegetables before storage.

Don't keep onions, garlic, sweet potatoes, squash or
pumpkins in damp places.

Don't seal grains and dried nuts that haven't been
completely dried in tightly closed containers.

Carrots and radishes often store best in damp sand or
damp sawdust.

During growing season don't give storage fruits or root
crops a lot of nitrogen fertilizer.

If you have several storage spots keep a map of what is
where.

Eat what you store. Don't begrudge small amounts of
spoilage. You're still way better off than with
normal supermarket produce.

You do know, of course, that some vegetables need no
cooling to store well. These would include pumpkins, winter
squash, sweet potatoes, and dried hot peppers. Both pumpkins
and squash should be cured before storage. This involves dry-
ing them a bit in the sun, or near a source of heat in the house,
for 10 to 14 days so the rind toughens. They should be stored
then with their stems intact. Though pumpkins won't last as
long (maybe that's why we have pumpkin pie at Thanksgiving
and Christmas?) most squashes will last till spring under
proper storage conditions. The exceptions here are acorn
squashes which should not be cured, and which should be
stored at lower temperatures than the others. But even among
the acorns there are exceptions. Read your seed catalogues
carefully.

Green tomatoes also store well in warmer spaces. A few
years ago, at the end of the season when they were in abun-

dance, I scored a full cardboard box of green tomatoes for a ridiculous $1.00 at our local farmer's market. I didn't do anything to them at all, didn't wrap them, put them in a sunny window, cool them or keep them warm. I just left them out in the box on a table and enjoyed them for a full month. First I had them as fried green tomatoes. Then as they ripened I enjoyed them as slicing tomatoes or ate them out of hand with sprinkled salt. Gave away a dozen or two also.

Listen, construct yourself a little root cellar even if it's just something you put together in the corner of your basement, or an old refrigerator you bury with a couple of bales of straw and a tarp on top. It's a fine, comfortable feeling to know that you have months of healthy, organic eating close at hand that will not go bad if the electricity goes out for a couple of days or weeks or months. It's satisfying to know you are doing your part to conserve energy and lessen pollution. It's a step back to basics. It's a step away from the madness of industrial life.

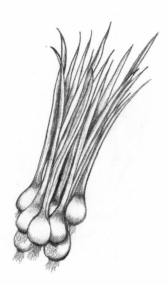

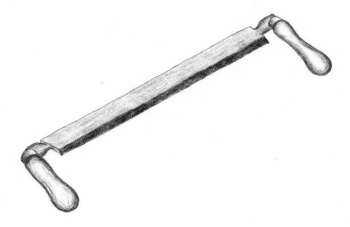

CHAPTER 15
The garden house

Back in the mid 1980's a friend and I built one of my more interesting and promising – yet least successful – underground structures. Though at first we called it Irvin's house, the name evolved into the Flat Land House because it is the only underground house built on flat land on my forty-five acres. I have since come to think of it as The Garden House, because not only is it located near my original garden site, but it also has a built-in greenhouse and a large root cellar attached. It was both a gardener's and a survivalist's dream – sort of an all-in-one life support system. It is longer in use as a house, greenhouse or root cellar, however. Here's the story of our triumphs and blunders.

We built the garden house on the site of the original earth-sheltered greenhouse. This site is on the only relatively flat seven acres of my forty, and near the only source of running water. It is one of the few spots on the land which was accessible by vehicle and is in the area closest to snowplowed and graded county roads. There are also telephone and electricity available. Unfortunately, it is shaded by a high ridge to the south. When the sun gets low in the winter sky, the shadow creeps out from the ridge until sometime around mid-October when the site gets only an hour or two of direct sunlight. That doesn't mean that the plants die – some of them in the attached greenhouse would live clear through the winter – but it does mean that they would stop growing. Nevertheless, the greenhouses there would double the growing season and, in addition, would extend the harvest life of the plants two to five more months.

Though the garden house is still in existence, it is mostly a shell now, used primarily for storage. We made a number of mistakes on it which, combined with a lack of time and migration of activities to other areas on the land, led to neglect and structural decay. But the concept was sound, and if I ever get the time and money, I'll try to resurrect it before it is beyond saving.

The garden house had three sections, two of which were earth-sheltered. The main section was 12'x12' and was the living quarters. "Twelve by twelve!" you will exclaim. "That's the size of some walk-in closets!" Right. And that was our first and greatest mistake. Why we built that room to such a miniscule size is a tale in itself which we will relate in a minute.

To the south side of this shed roof house, the high side with the largest expanse of windows, was an attached greenhouse of 4'x12' floor space and varying head room of up to five feet. Though not an earth-sheltered greenhouse, it nevertheless got some earth sheltering benefits which we will discuss in a moment also.

Log carrier

The third section of the house was an attached 8'x8' root cellar. Access to it was through a secret panel which fascinated kids and adults alike. It was enormous fun to show this off, and so it quickly became a secret no more. But it is something to consider doing yourself if you think – as do many – that a day of reckoning is coming for civilization, America in particular. In that event it could be worth your life to have a place to hide and shelter your food and tools, and your family.

The roof of the garden house was earthen-covered, except the greenhouse. You had to descend a few steps to get into the living quarters and a few more to get into the root cellar. The floor of the root cellar was about five feet below ground level and had two to three feet of earth cover on the roof.

The greenhouse was at ground level and had neither earth cover nor berm. So how does that fit into a book on earth-sheltered greenhouses? Because it still got earth-sheltering benefits since it was attached to a partially-sunken, earth-sheltered structure. Besides standard benefit that any greenhouse attached to a dwelling gets – warmth from the heated dwelling in the cold months – the dwelling this green-house was attached to acted as a massive cold-sink. All I had to do was open a window separating the greenhouse and the dwelling and the cold air accumulating in the greenhouse would flow down into the house to be replaced by convection-propelled, warmer air. A greenhouse attached to a normal frame house does not get this benefit. An unheated frame house without a basement is losing heat from all directions, including from the crawl space below. But I could leave the garden house for days in freezing weather without the plants freezing as long as I left that window open.

If you are attaching a greenhouse, you may be able to do something of the same if the structure you are adding it to has a basement with windows. Just open those windows and let the cold air drain down. To make a really effective system, place the greenhouse where you can also open a window on the first floor which will allow warm air from the house to flow in to replace the cold air spilling into the basement. If this is not working well, try opening the door from the house to the basement also, to promote the current of air.

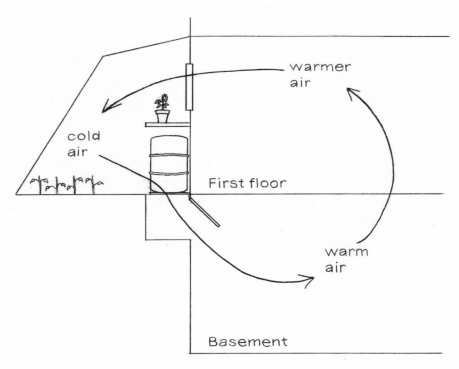

You may be tempted to try excavating to make the attached greenhouse also earthen-sheltered. Though it might work well on a home with a basement, particularly where there are no basement windows, it could prove disastrous if you tried it on a home with a crawl space. The footings on such a home should go down to the frost line (three foot in N. Idaho) so that the earth beneath can't freeze and expand and crumble or buckle them. By digging down next to them you might inadvertently expose the earth below to just such freezing in extreme conditions, say if you were unable to heat your house for several weeks because of power blackout, or because you left for the winter.

Now as to the problems which have caused the garden house to be mostly abandoned. Let me caution you again not to judge my structures by their flaws. And kindly do not judge me by my errors. I emphasize my errors and flaws so that you do not make the same ones – just as I emphasize my triumphs so that you might be equally triumphant. Despite some bungling, my places work, and they work far better than most conventional structures.

The major problem, as mentioned, is that the place was too small for comfortable daily living. Though the responsibility for this and all the other problems rests solely on my shoulders, the immediate cause was a wonderful character named Irvin who lived on my land for a year-and-a-half.

Irvin was a character of the first order. He was one of a kind, one of the originals. Though only in his early forties, he was beginning to go bald and had sort of an old man's high, whiney voice. But the thing that set him apart most distinctly was that he continually wore a pull-over-the-head robe that he had hand-sewn from old blankets. On his feet were second-hand store shoes and no socks. Whether he wore underwear I cannot say. I never saw him wash any nor any hanging out to dry. I never saw him bathe, either, and don't ever recall him in the sauna. I seem to recall a pungent odor about him, though nothing truly repelling. Perhaps he sponge-bathed every couple of weeks or months.

His diet consisted of anything he was given or could scrounge or forage. He ate out of my garden in the warm months and the greenhouse in the colder ones. He also had large bunches of dried, edible wild foods such as lambs quarter and wild lettuce hanging from every available rafter. When I'd return from town once or twice a week I'd have treats for him; jars of peanut butter and jelly, perhaps, or a couple of cans of chili. But what kept him going – what gave him his calories – was my stored wheat. He'd grind it on a hand grinder, add a little water and knead it so the coarse flour was in a primitive sort of dough which he'd store in a warm place for days to let the natural yeast work up. Then he'd bake it on a wood stove top or even over an open fire in a cast iron fry pan with a lid. Though there was frequently a black crust on the bottom of the loaf which only Irvin would eat, it was otherwise quite good, especially warm with a little butter and honey. During his time on my land he went through an entire 55-gallon steel drum of wheat berries. I later perfected his baking technique by greasing regular bread pans and setting them on four nickels to raise them off the stove top, then covering the whole thing with an inverted, stainless steel bowl to make an oven.

Irvin was a super-duper Christian. I never saw him read anything other than the Bible. He wouldn't touch money because it has a graven image on it, and the Bible warns against graven images. He would not let his picture be taken for the same reason. His association with other Christians was severely limited because they were not pure enough. But he could associate with me because I was a heathen – I was into Buddhism, Hinduism, Yoga and A Course in Miracles. The Bible, according to Irvin, says it's okay to associate with us heathen because we don't know any better but you had best not associate with impure Christians. At some point in the past Irvin had been committed to a mental hospital, but I think that lasted for only a couple of weeks. His descriptions of his discussions with the shrinks would make you smile, even laugh out loud. I had visions of the good doctors throwing up their hands and yelling "get this guy out of here, he's crazy!" Irvin was still resentful and fearful of his experience, and when he left my place I told him to call if he landed back in, and I would do what I could to get him out.

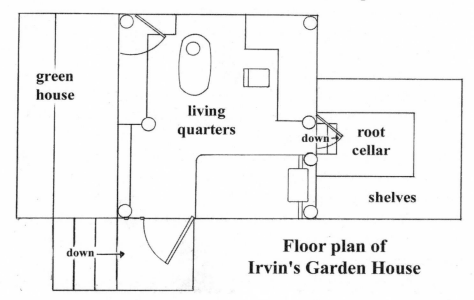

green house

living quarters

down→

root cellar

shelves

down ——→

Floor plan of Irvin's Garden House

When he was interested in a project, Irvin could turn out a decent piece of work – sometimes. He was great at organizing clutter, for example, and since clutter is one my great failings, that worked out quite well. But he would spend hundreds of hours on projects of dubious value. For one, he dug up by hand half an acre of my most productive pasture. He measured it meticulously and marked it with sunken posts. He put it into "raised bed" agriculture to grow wheat. Though some of the wheat did come up, I recall only a single sheath that produced grain. I stumbled over those raised beds for years afterwards and could no longer run my horse there for fear she would stumble and perhaps break a leg, or fall with me beneath. And that pasture was pretty much ruined for graze for some years afterward, too.

But it was the garden house that was Irvin's legacy. We worked on it together with Irvin doing most of the digging, siding and roofing, plus the doors and windows. I did the design, gathered the materials and set most of the posts, and did the girders and roof beams. I did the *most* of the design, that is. Irving and I had an altercation about the size of the main room. He insisted that it be small. I wanted it four feet wider, another forty-eight square feet. At that insistence he literally threw a tantrum. "I don't want to heat a big house!"

"It's not going to be big!" It's still going to be tiny. The size you want you'll hardly be able to turn around in there."

"I don't want to heat a big house!"

"Listen, even if we do it my size, when you fire up a tin stove in there it's going to roast you out. You'll have a window open in there all winter!"

"I'm not going to heat a big house," he yelled, swinging his arms and stamping his sockless, wingtipped, second-hand shoes.

After a couple of days of this sort of exchange, I gave in. It was to be his house after all, and he was doing more than half of the building. But, as time proved, it was really too small for any normal person. You couldn't get a usual table in there, not even a card table, or an easy chair for that matter. Later, when my girlfriend lived in there with her toddler, I built a fence around the stove to make sure one-year old Steve didn't fall against it and maybe disfigure himself for life with a burn scar. That took up just enough other space in the room to make one side of the stove impassable and two more sides so narrow that a person had to shuffle sideways to get past. If Darla was cooking or serving a meal, Steve and I had to stay on the bed. There simply wasn't room for us all on the floor together.

Irvin was to be my caretaker, that winter he was here, while I went out on the road lecturing. We had the house nearly completed a few days before I left. All that remained was to put in the windows and door and Irvin would be snug all winter. He was the son of a carpenter and had learned the trade at his daddy's knee. He was masterful, twenty times the carpenter I am. But, when I began outlining how he could finish the place while I was gone, he threw another tantrum.

"I'm not going to do it!"

"You're not? Why in the world not?

"I might do it wrong."

"Nonsense. You are a vastly better carpenter than me. Your wrong is better than my right. If you really screw anything up we can rip it out in the spring and redo it."

peavey

"I won't know what windows go where."

"I'll draw you a diagram. Plans. We can number the windows with a pencil."

"I might run out of nails or something."

"I'll see that you have everything you need. I'll even leave some money with the neighbors and they can pick up anything else you need in town."

"I'm not going to do it. It'll be too cold to work on it."

"Oh, bull. You can tack some polyethylene from the roof to the ground and work inside it with a fire going in the stove. You'll be toasty. If for some reason you can't complete a section, you can use the polyethylene for a temporary wall or window till spring. I've lived in places like that when I was ski bumming in the high Colorado Mountains. It works."

"I'm not going to do it!" He was stamping his wing tips again.

"Then where do you expect to live? This is northern Idaho, man. These winters get cold."

"I want to live in your greenhouse."

"In my greenhouse!! Are you out of your mind? My tomatoes freeze out there the second week in December, and so will you."

"I'll bring the stove up."

"Right, and you will be packing all your water and food and kerosene for your lamp in, too. And I'll tell you it's a bitch to try to get firewood in on that hillside in the snow. You'll slip all over the place. On the other hand if you live in this place I can probably squeeze in an afternoon with my truck and chainsaw and the two of us can bring in most of your wood for the winter. The rest of it you can get in over flat ground."

"I won't do it. I want to live in your greenhouse."

By this time I was thoroughly exasperated. But I had a hole card.

"I thought you said you didn't want to heat a big house. That greenhouse is at least six times the size of this place. And the roof is just a few millimeters of plastic not a couple of inches of wood and a couple of feet of earth. The heat's going to radiate right out. Be reasonable, man."

I vowed not to call him crazy or an idiot or swear at him or yell. He was stamping his feet again and would not be

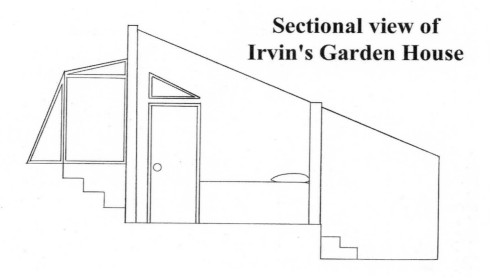

Sectional view of Irvin's Garden House

swayed. So, incredibly, he went through the winter in the greenhouse, hauling in his firewood in his arms, and breaking it or sawing it by hand. He had to have been miserable.

When I returned in the spring, it was I who was miserable, or at least angry. I'd assigned him just a few jobs – but they needed doing: water-barring the road that led down a small hill onto the land, and getting a few inches of earth onto the polyethylene on the roof of the house to protect it – maybe ten hours work altogether. But he had done neither, and the road washed out and the polyethylene turned out later to have been punctured, so the roof leaked. And of course he hadn't finished the house. Then, when I discovered that he had inadvertently cut the buried telephone line to my house by digging cat-holes rather than using the latrine as requested, I seethed and was doubtless discourteous to him.

To Irvin's credit he clenched his jaw, and fixed or completed everything as best he could. Then he left my land in a self-justified huff.

Four days later I entered the local bar a couple of miles from my place, and as I walked down to find an empty stool, every single person turned and gave me a huge grin and a big hello. I was considerably flattered and pleased. As a raging environmentalist in a logger town, I have often not been everyone's favorite. But that day everyone was clearly delighted to see me. How popular could a guy get?

I settled into a beer and noticed that there was no conversation in the place, but everyone was still grinning. Then a character named Way Davis became their spokesman: "Say Mike, we met that friend of yours, that Irvin fellow. He's been hanging around the yard sale across the street the last few days. Quite a fellow. Yep, quite a guy, that Irvin."

Everybody down the bar was grinning into their drinks and darting quick glances at me.

Then the lady sitting next to Way said, "You know Mike, we've always considered you eccentric. But now, after meeting that Irvin guy, we realize *you're perfectly normal*!"

After leaving mine, Irvin landed at the place of another friend, Jim, who told me later that he had stayed with him for a month and did his share of the work. But when Jim would prepare a meal, Irvin would take his plate and eat in the root cellar. Jim was a Christian but wasn't pure enough to eat with.

I was to see Irvin ten years later at the 1997 Oregon Rainbow Gathering. Spotted him a hundred yards away in his hand-sewn robe and second-hand shoes. Couldn't miss him. I went up and said hello but he didn't recognize me.

"My name's not Irvin any more. I've changed it to Ebenezer."

"Oh, well Ebenezer, don't you remember staying on my forty acres in North Idaho? You were there a year and a half. You came to me from Brett and Lorrie's. When you left my place, you stayed with Jim and ate all your meals in his root cellar."

Blank looks. He doesn't remember.

"Let's see. How about planting a half acre of wheat in

raised beds?"

No recollection.

"How about the afternoon you ate for three hours straight in Ethyl Mae Eddy's kitchen. Ate up stuff she wanted to get rid of in her freezer."

That draws a blank, too. (Ethel Mae never forgot it, though; "I have never in my life seen a man eat like that …")

"Well, how about the winter you lived in my greenhouse?"

Head up like a bird dog picking up a scent. Then a breakthrough. "Brother Mike!" he yelled. "We built a house together!"

"Yeah, we did," I said, returning the Rainbow hug he was giving me.

A few minutes later writer Denis Johnson, at his first Gathering, joined us. Always appreciative of a good character, Denis was duly impressed by Ebenezer, who rambled on in his  creaky old man's voice about his life and his "new parents," which was apparently how he was thinking of the people who hosted him those days.

Denis' smile broadened considerably, as did mine, no doubt, when Irvin-Ebenezer talked about the Rainbow "sister" he had met whom he was hoping to marry. Visualizing Ebenezer as stable family man -- and the lady who would consent to marry him -- was delicious. Though I tried to get Ebenezer to hang with us a while longer, he soon insisted he had to be off to find the sister again. And it was with real regret that we watched him shuffle off in his robe and second-hand, sock-less, wingtip shoes, in quest of his new love. Ebenezer writes every couple of years to Brett who has offered to give me the address should I ever decide to invite Ebenezer back. I'm building, and I might. He's a really fine carpenter.

West view of Irvin-Ebenezer's Garden House

Upper left: Mike, in 1976, sets a post in the cold-sink of his first earth-sheltered greenhouse. *Upper right:* Josh, a volunteer, rakes out growing soil. *Center left:* The little greenhouse nears completion. The "bubble" in the glazing occurred due to inexperience. The opening was later stuffed with old clothes for insulation and covered with earth. "It weren't pretty, but it worked." *Lower right:* Mike works in the greenhouse two months after the unheated above-ground greenhouses in the area had frozen out.

Above and center: Mike examines tomatoes and kale that are still thriving the earliest days of December in the hillside greenhouse. *Lower left:* Close up of the same plants, same day. *Lower right:* On December 17th occasional employee, Stephanie, examines plants after a week of temperatures dipping into the lower teens. To our astonishment we find one tomato plant that is still alive, though struggling. The adjacent kale was still alive and harvestable a month later despite some zero degree nights and no water for six weeks.

The photos on page 165 are all of the hillside greenhouse.

Top shows construction phase just as the walls begin to go up. The polyethylene is in place and ready to be stretched towards the roof. Which means the first course or two of boards are in place pinning down the poly. The walls will go up evenly — a course on the north, backfilled, a course on the south , etc. — to keep the structure from being forced off plumb as it would have been had one wall been put in at a time and backfilled.

Center left: The rafters are in place and await trimming. Purlins will go between them to keep the corrugated single-sheet plastic glazing from sagging.

Center right: In 2003 we lined most of the growing beds with 1/4 inch galvanized wire mesh, as a #$%&** gopher deterrent. So far it has worked. The volunteer in the striped shirt was a retired U.S. Marine who advocated bombing the capital of each nation in Europe that refused passage of U.S. troops and equipment enroute to the invasion of Iraq. This concept was discussed at high volume, though without fisti-cuffs. We even managed to part amicably the next day.

Below: The 20th Century earth-sheltered solar hillside greenhouse as it looks in the 21st Century. The protrusion in the center is for a second-door airlock (which never did work effectively — even less so after thirty years of warping, benign neglect and carpenter ant colonization. As a whole however, the greenhouse still shelters just fine.

You may wonder, wisely, what those boards are doing suspended on edge near the floor running north to south from the bottom of the north posts to the middle posts. Those are to keep the north posts from "hinging" for this was one of our structures built with the "pier" system as described in Chapter Five. Despite the fact that it wasn't true bone support (they were nailed to the sides), they still managed to do their assignment and no posts hinged. They provided a second benefit by providing support for boards laying across them to be walked up on when working on plants on the bench. This way the plants beneath were not trampled and the earth not compacted.

The earth-sheltered solar greenhouse at Telelestai Ranch (facing page) near Sacramento, California, was built by Luke Vorpagel with the PSP system in 2006 with material scrounged up with David Fairall. David had built a shed twenty years earlier with material salvaged from old wooden garage doors, so the two men called construction companies till they found one that replaced wood garage doors with metal. Since the company would have otherwise had to haul the material to the dump, they were happy to give it away free. 2x4's salvaged from the doors were screwed together to make 4x4's for the posts and the plywood became the greenhouse PSP shoring. The sliding glass doors used for the glazing were equally free after they located a company that retrofitted old homes with new doors and windows. Racks to hold trays of starts were built from salvaged angle iron. Altogether the out of pocket cost of the greenhouse—sheet polyethylene, garbage bags, sealant, latches and hardware to hold the angle iron together, plus truck gas to gather the materials, was well under $100, probably closer to $50.

Right: Luke Vorpagel digs out the cold-sink of his earth-sheltered solar greenhouse at Tetelestai Ranch, California.

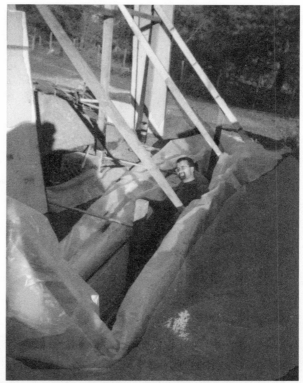

Below: Ian and Hannah Fairall hold freshly planted seedling trays ready to go into the completed greenhouse.

CHAPTER 16
Designing your own greenhouse

We haven't given you much in the way of ready-made greenhouse plans in this book, and there is a reason for this. Each person's climate, site, yield expectations, building material funds, time to build, time to scrounge materials, carpentry skills, or financial ability to hire carpenters are all different. My trying to fit your needs and circumstances into a one size and model greenhouse is much like the single-width-size shoes they are selling in many of the mail order catalogs these days — medium size "D," take it or leave it. (How long before they come out with only size 9D, take it or leave it?) Well, sorry, but I refuse to cram you into a size 9D greenhouse. Or to even give you a choice between 7D, 9D, and 11D. Instead, I'm going to expand and clarify the design concepts we've explained here so far so that you may design your greenhouse to your own needs and circumstances. This, hopefully, will save you our 30 years of trial and error.

First of all, you must answer the all-important question of whether you are going to try for winter growth. This is as opposed to merely harvesting the hardy plants that you grew in the late summer and fall that will stay alive and dormant in your earth-sheltered greenhouse all winter. Now, unless your proposed project is to be built in the warmer climes, or is to be attached to the south side of a house, or is to have supplementary heat and grow lights, I suggest that you don't try for winter growth. Careful planning will leave you with a greenhouse full of wonderful, organic edibles that you may harvest all winter without their needing to continue to grow. If you have done things right, your hardies will still get enough light and warmth to hibernate comfortably while staying a tasty and nutritious table ready. To try for more growth without supplemental light and heat is, in most instances, to swim against the current.

(This doesn't mean, incidentally, that you can't still grow plants during those short-light, cold months of November, December, January and February. You certainly can. You may grow them in the house in pots moved in from the greenhouse, or start new plants in the house in January for transfer into the greenhouse in late February. Your house likely has south-facing windows for sunshine, is heated all winter, and, if it is on the grid, has enough power for supplemental grow lights. Your home and your greenhouse can work in partnership.)

So let's look at some northern latitude greenhouse designs. We'll start with a critical look at my hillside greenhouse. Though effective, it is far from perfect. I want you to learn from my trial and error mistakes so that you don't make the same ones. And, of course, I want you to repeat my trial and error triumphs.

I could see right off when we got done digging the hole that we were going to have a problem with headroom while standing on the platform in the cold-sink. Though the north wall was a solid seven feet from hillside surface to growing bed, where the grow bed ended on the south side there was only a foot or two of depth. So we raised the roof a couple of feet above ground level to the south. This turned out to be a very good thing because when we glazed that couple of feet we discovered that for several months around the winter solstice it is through those couple of feet of glazing that we get most of the sunshine. The sun is at such a low angle (17.56 degrees at winter solstice) that it mostly just bounces off the glazed roof and will do so for  several months during the winter. That's when the roof is not snow-covered. When it is, we keep it there for insulation. Why not if the rays would just bounce off anyway? So there is a lesson here: in the northern latitudes have some vertical or heavily-slanted glazing to the south if you wish any appreciable winter sun. It may not be enough sun for growth, but it will help warm the greenhouse and keep the plants alive.

Ventilation has been a problem at times in the hillside greenhouse. Though the entrance door in the south wall into the cold-sink platform lets in probably enough air, I hadn't factored in enough exhaust vents. There were only two, one at each of the north wall corners. They were only about one and a half by two feet each for a total of six square feet. I should have had triple that. My plants suffered as a result and protested by drooping, nearly dying, on hot days. They weren't doing any growing then. Not good gardening.

Though the walls were fairly well earthen-covered on

The **HILLSIDE GREENHOUSE** is approximately ten feet wide by 27 feet long. The grow bed is seven or eight feet wide. The north wall is about seven foot high and the cold sink eight foot deep. A few inches of the back-filled earth outside of the north wall have apparently settled, for there are four to eight inches of exposure there (more at the ends where we excavated a foot and a half for the vents.) In the cold days of winter we lay a polyethylene strip against the exposure and rake some earth, leaves, needles and pine cones down against it for insulation. In the summer we pull it off and appreciate the extra openings for ventilation. It helps to make up for our miscalculation of vent number and size, our underestimation of need.

I keep vacillating in my mind about the correct year we built this greenhouse, but at the moment I believe it was 1978 or 1979. We used trees off my land for the posts, short pieces of imperfect lumber (thrown away by the saw mills in those days) called "millends", and dug it by hand ourselves, myself and volunteers. Nails, hinges, screws, door latches and other miscellaneous hardware items were mostly salvaged. Our only costs were for the glazing (Filon) $115.00, the rafters it was nailed to, the (incorrectly placed) girders they were notched into, the framing around the "wall windows" and doors $100.00, polyethylene (probably 4 mil. — would use 6 mil. now) $20.00, corrugated sponge rubber to insulate and make air tight the ends of the glazing $8.00, caulking $5.00, a couple of days labor for the carpenter who set the rafters and the glazing $100.00, beer and food for volunteers $30.00, plus $10.00 for miscellaneous and things we are forgetting. By my reckoning that comes to a very ball park estimate of $388.00. I re-glazed it in 1999 for an estimated $300.00. Had I glazed it also in 1989 for perhaps $200.00 making the '90's productive, that would have come out to a total of $888.00 for approximately 30 years use, or $29.60 per year, $2.47 per month or a touch over 8 cents per day. At today's prices it might come out to 25 cents per day.

the north, south and east sides, the west side had a ten-foot expanse of bare wood exposed to the air. This was caused by the ridge dropping off to the west as well as south. That bare wall was/is uninsulated. I had vaguely planned for years to put some windows there. The greenhouse is in a small clearing in the woods, and the west is a little more clear and would have afforded some additional, badly-needed sunlight.

But I never got to it, nor did I ever get to insulating that wall. The closest I came to insulation was a thin, single covering of building paper, tar paper, which, though it helped to keep the wind from whistling through the gaps between the boards, provided little in the way of insulation. You would have thought a guy could have at least stapled up some layers of cardboard there. Nevertheless, it is a testament to the effectiveness of earth-sheltering-with-cold-sink that, despite that uninsulated wall, the greenhouse is a number of months more productive than a comparable, above-ground greenhouse.

This all suggests, however, that we discuss something we have so far not covered, and which is of importance when you design your greenhouse. It is the question of whether to put windows on the east and west walls of the structure. You would assume the answer to be "yes," but the authorities on solar greenhouses seem divided on the question with the sentiment edging towards "no".

The nay sayers have a point. The east and west walls are each exposed to only half of the solar energy – because the sun only reaches each of them half the day – that is experienced by a similar amount of glazing on the south wall. Yet east and west each lose as much heat at night as a similar area of glazing on the south. And they lose heat during the half of the day in which they get no sun, unlike the south which is gaining heat throughout most of the day. I will add another point: The winter sun has a different arc in the sky than in the summer. We all know that it is not nearly as close to being overhead at noon in the winter as in the summer. But city folk, with their view of the setting sun blocked by tall buildings, frequently fail to recognize that the seasonal suns set at quite different points on the horizon. If the sun were to be directly overhead at noon, as it is in Mexico and the Bahamas at the summer solstice, it would have a 180-degree arc rising directly in the east and setting directly in the west. But in the wintertime in some places it will rise in the southeast and set in the southwest with an arc of only 90 degrees. This results in the sun hitting those east and west windows at highly oblique angles, causing much of it to glance off. So in the winter when you need it the most, those east and west windows give you the least.

There is yet another factor to consider here should you decide to go ahead with east and west windows: The placement of the windows can result in up to three times as much sun coverage on the south sections of the east and west walls as on the north sections. I'm not even going to try to explain this. Study the illustration and you should see why.

Ergo, if I were to consider those east and west windows in cold country, I would definitely do so only for those on the south portion of the walls. I'd berm earth up on the north section, insulate it and cover it with polyethylene and some more dirt and turn it into a heat-sink area. For windows or other glazing in the southern part of the walls, you can be sure I'd have portable insulation panels ready to slip into place. Those east and west windows make more sense in the more southerly latitudes where the sun rises and sets at all times closer to the 180 degree angle.

Given a choice between either the east or west walls for windows, I'd probably choose the east to help the plants wake up in the morning. Then, too, on a hot day shade from the west wall in the afternoon could be a plant blessing.

Besides more light and headroom there can be another

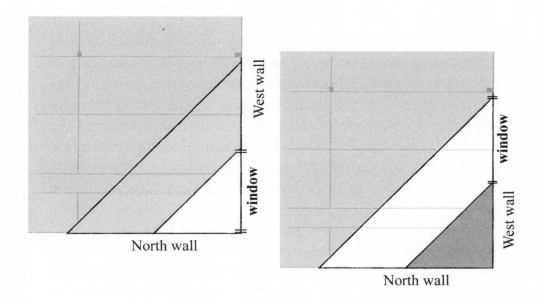

West wall

window

North wall

window

West wall

North wall

reason for raising the south side of the roof above earth level. This is when you want to catch that rain off the roof and run it into barrels for later irrigation in the grow beds, or, failing that, when you want to divert it away from the structure altogether. If you have running water on the site, and don't need to store it, and are on a hillside, you can just let the rain water run off the glazing and down the hill and be done with it. (I'd probably put a strip of galvanized sheet metal for the first foot or two to divert the water away from the sunken greenhouse wall).

On flat land that water could be a problem if you don't do something with it. You will, of course, berm at least six inches around all the walls of the flatland greenhouse, right? Including around the stairwell down to the cold-sink platform? Good. You've made a dike. That should keep water from entering and flooding the structure from the surface, especially during spring breakup. But if the ground becomes saturated, you might have water entry from below or from any improperly-sealed seams or perforation in the polyethylene. It would pay you to divert that water away from the greenhouse.

In order then to do this, you will need to raise the roof enough inches to allow for an attached rain gutter and its necessary pitch, or fall. That is to say it needs to be lower on the end of the gutter where the water exits. And unless you can figure out a way to exit the water directly into a hose from the very end of the gutter wall, you are going to have to allow space between the gutter and earth for a hose attachment and the first few inches of hose where it makes a turn And you

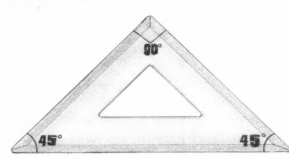

must allow enough height for the hose to drain out fifty or so feet away from the greenhouse.

Or you can run that hose into the greenhouse and store the water in barrels as I did. This served a twofold purpose: It made for passive solar heat storage, and it gave me irrigation water for my plants.

My system was/is far from perfect, but it works. One problem was elevation. Even with the raised roof there was precious little fall between the ends of the gutters and the 55-gallon drums I used for water storage. And that was when I laid them on their sides in shallow excavated areas on either end of the greenhouse.

The side which lies on the ground (on boards to help prevent rust) is maybe eight inches lower than the grow bed depth. This allows me to both fill the barrels from the gutter hose, and to remove that hose and insert a shorter one to siphon the water into five-gallon pails resting on the platform in the cold-sink for use in watering the plants.

A second problem was screening the water from the pine, fir and tamarack needles which eagerly clog up the hose. At first I tried just screening up the hole at the bottom of the gutter. Didn't work. The needles dammed up the screen, and the precious water overflowed and was lost. Then I tried also bending wire screen to fit the gutter a couple of inches in front of the exit hole, but that plugged up too. Finally, I left the first two screens in place and also screened off the entire top of the gutter. That works fairly well if I clean all three screens periodically.

A hose coupling needs to be secured to the exit hole in the gutter. I think we soldered ours on. The galvanized gutter metal was probably too thin to be welded. If you can't figure this one out take the problem to a machine shop.

Post/shoring/polyethylene construction with a cold-sink offers a unique opportunity to divide your glazed roof into two sections, the highest one of which is great for catching water for use. It's high enough you should have no trouble filling 55-gallon drums which are standing upright for use as heat sinks. Upright also means you should also be able to draw from them for plant watering. There are a number of pumps sold which would do the job admirably. Lehman's offers several. If you are to go into this wholeheartedly, it might pay to get one of the professional hand fuel pumps that loggers and others use to pump diesel out of tanks in the back of their pickups for use in their cats and skidders. Individual plywood covers holding potted plants on top of each barrel should be easily removed on watering and filling days. Otherwise, a permanent bench on top of all the barrels might be drilled through over each bung hole to facilitate the filling and emptying. This is if you can only get sealed top barrels with bungs. Some 55-gallon barrels have tops you can remove easily. Then you can just dip the water out.

When the barrels are filled, by the way, there is no reason why you can't let the hose from the gutter lie in the spaces between the crop rows and let it saturate the ground. Move it as needed during heavy rains.

The reason the P/S/P method with cold-sink lends itself well to a two-part or two-angle roof lies in the structure beneath. There are three sets of posts in these greenhouses. One holds up the north wall of the growing area, and two are in the cold-sink. It is the north wall of the cold-sink, the middle set of posts as it were, that is of particular interest here.

This middle set of posts always does triple duty. It holds back the earth of the cold-sink north wall. It balances out the earth pressure, the lateral thrust of the south wall. And it provides support for the walkway above the rabbits, compost or whatever you have in the cold-sink. It is that walkway, remember, that makes it possible for you to work in comfort on your southernmost three or four feet of plants in the main growing bed.

Now let's give the posts a fourth function. There are a couple of ways of changing the pitch on that front part of your glazing. One is to play with the width of your cold-sink. Two foot or four foot? Buy yourself a pad of ¼ inch graph paper, an architect's ruler, a plastic protractor and a plastic square. With these you can design almost any kind of a structure with ease. Or maybe you know how to do it on the computer. Anyway, play around. You not only have the width of the cold-sink to play with but also the height of the main part of the glazing to help you find your desired pitch. If you wish to have sun entering through your steeply-pitched section at pretty much right angles during the equinoxes, look up your latitude or closest city. Put the center of your protractor on the very top of the south wall of your plan with the bottom of the protractor at right angles to the wall. Then mark the reading for your city in the tables and chart on pages 188-189. What we've used for the two greenhouse illustrations in the next chapter is 48 degrees, roughly that of Chicago. We've also designed them with the idea in mind that the steeply angled part over the cold-sink be of the right dimensions to be glazed with 6-foot 7-inch used sliding glass doors, though you may of course glaze your own greenhouse with any appropriate material of any dimensions suitable.

Those posts are in an ideal placement on the larger greenhouses to support glazings of two different angles and perhaps two different materials. Over the growing bed area you will probably want a gentler pitch on the roof to keep the back wall from being humongously high. This will also allow good summer sun penetration. It is in the summer and fall, remember, when you do your growing for those plants which you harvest during the winter dormant period. My rule of thumb here on the Idaho/Canadian border is to have winter leafy greens like lettuce and Swiss chard planted by August 1st when I (but not my city guests who occasionally think I am delusional) notice the earliest signs of autumn. Such signs as the geese circling on training runs, a few

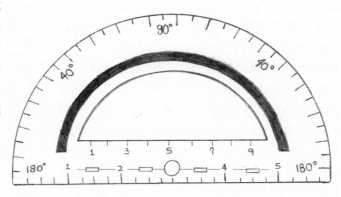

ground cover plants turning color, earlier sunsets, and nights that are crisper. Slower maturing plants like kale and cabbage I have started earlier. These are all second crop plants, for I have been eating first crop items from the greenhouse since March — two months before most gardeners in our area even begin planting.

At any rate, here are these posts that you must have to hold back the north wall of your cold-sink, plus two other functions.   By simply cutting them longer, long enough to reach the roof, you can give them a fourth vital function.   You can have them become the structural members that make the change in pitch of the glazing possible.   This can give you a greenhouse that utilizes the sun's rays to the utmost.

What is the pitch most beneficial for you?   That depends.   But I will make this suggestion.   If you pitch the front glazing so that the sun will strike it at 90 degrees at the Spring and Autumn equinox, you will have maximum sun exposure at two times of the year when you need it the most.   Furthermore, you will have excellent exposure for thirty days or more on either side of the equinox, for a total of four good months in otherwise less than optimum conditions.

The other eight months?   Well, four of them are the warmest months with the longest days and best growing conditions generally, so you needn't worry about them.   They have that big wide expanse of glazing on the roof which is pitched pretty good for the summer sun.   Except for overheating, those months can take care of themselves.

So that leaves just November, December, January and February to worry about.   November has never been a problem for me in the hillside greenhouse despite our 2000-foot elevation, proximity to Canada and cloudy Northwest winter skies. It may be a revisionist memory, but I can not recall my tomatoes ever freezing out in November.   They seem to continue slowly ripening, in fact, despite the odds.   All the fruit the plants put on in a sudden burst of desperation when the days started getting shorter in August — the tomatoes everyone else would lose in their gardens and above ground greenhouses in the first frosts of September or October — would continue to struggle for me towards maturity.   Even those which couldn't make it could be picked in early December and fried green or held in a warm house to ripen into January.   Since they are so frost-vulnerable, tomatoes have always been my measure of success in the greenhouse. It goes without saying that most of my kale, cabbage, and even Swiss chard and lettuce would make it through the winter. And in late February or early March I'd be replanting again both with seed and starts from the house.

All this from a greenhouse that is single-pane, glazed at far than less desirable angles than we've been describing here, is uninsulated, has no animals other than mice and %*$&!# gophers and is run by an irresponsible, frequently intoxicated hippy. Ha! You, my friends, will do much, much better!

SPECIAL DESIGN FEATURES AND CONSIDERATIONS

Overcoming the Shade Problem in Earth Sheltered Greenhouses

We dealt extensively earlier in this book with the problems of shade caused by sheltering into the earth. Now we will give you some graphic examples of the way cold-sinks overcome them. We will give you four examples starting with Albuquerque, New Mexico, at a latitude of 35.05 and work north to Anchorage, Alaska, with a latitude of 61.17 and we'll see how either two-foot or four-foot wide cold sinks overcome most of the shade problems.

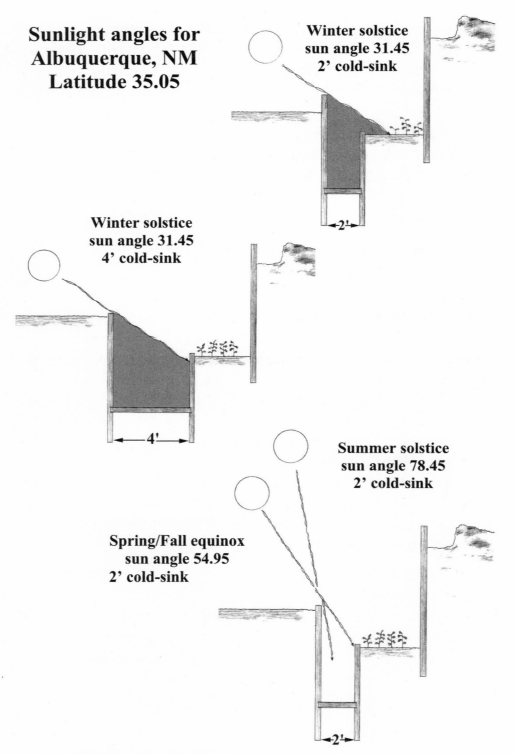

Sunlight angles for Albuquerque, NM Latitude 35.05

Winter solstice sun angle 31.45 2' cold-sink

Winter solstice sun angle 31.45 4' cold-sink

Summer solstice sun angle 78.45 2' cold-sink

Spring/Fall equinox sun angle 54.95 2' cold-sink

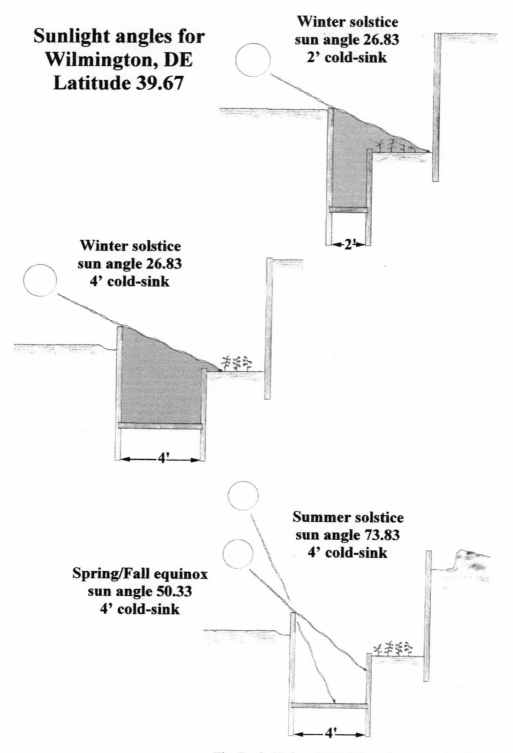

Sunlight angles for Wilmington, DE Latitude 39.67

Winter solstice sun angle 26.83 2' cold-sink

Winter solstice sun angle 26.83 4' cold-sink

Spring/Fall equinox sun angle 50.33 4' cold-sink

Summer solstice sun angle 73.83 4' cold-sink

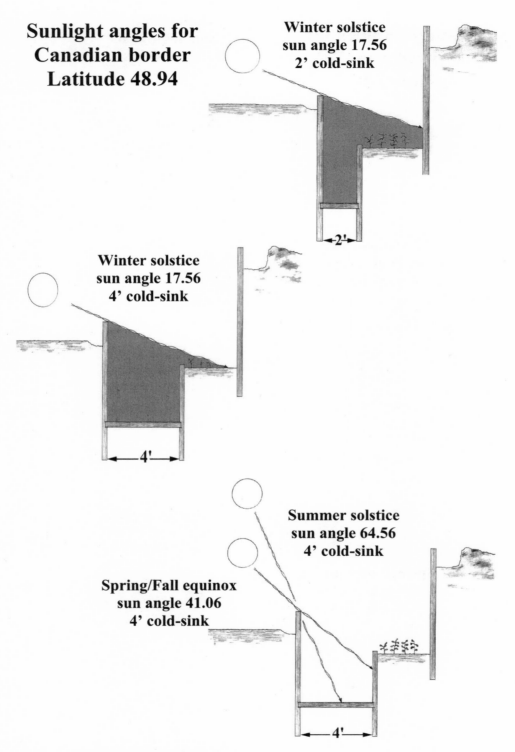

Sunlight angles for Canadian border Latitude 48.94

Winter solstice sun angle 17.56 2' cold-sink

2'

Winter solstice sun angle 17.56 4' cold-sink

4'

Summer solstice sun angle 64.56 4' cold-sink

Spring/Fall equinox sun angle 41.06 4' cold-sink

4'

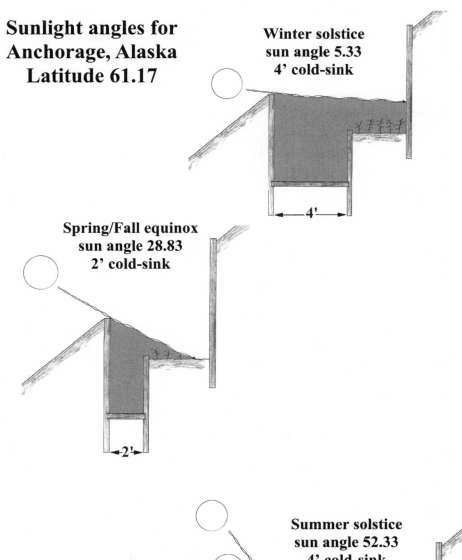

Sunlight angles for Anchorage, Alaska Latitude 61.17

Winter solstice
sun angle 5.33
4' cold-sink

4'

Spring/Fall equinox
sun angle 28.83
2' cold-sink

2'

Summer solstice
sun angle 52.33
4' cold-sink

Spring/Fall equinox
sun angle 28.83
4' cold-sink

4'

		Latitude	Spring Equinox	Summer Equinox	Fall Equinox	Winter Equinox
Canadian Border		48.94	41.06	64.56	41.06	17.56
City	**State**					
Albuquerque	NM	35.05	54.95	78.45	54.95	31.45
Anchorage	AK	61.17	28.83	52.33	28.83	5.33
Atlanta	GA	33.65	56.35	79.85	56.35	32.85
Baltimore	MD	39.18	50.82	74.32	50.82	27.32
Billings	MT	45.80	44.20	67.70	44.20	20.70
Birmingham	AL	33.57	56.43	79.93	56.43	32.93
Boise	ID	43.57	46.43	69.93	46.43	22.93
Boston	MA	42.37	47.63	71.13	47.63	24.13
Bridgeport	CT	41.17	48.83	72.33	48.83	25.33
Burlington	VT	44.47	45.53	69.03	45.53	22.03
Charleston	WV	38.37	51.63	75.13	51.63	28.13
Charlotte	NC	35.22	54.78	78.28	54.78	31.28
Cheyenne	WY	41.15	48.85	72.35	48.85	25.35
Chicago	IL	41.90	48.10	71.60	48.10	24.60
Columbia	SC	33.95	56.05	79.55	56.05	32.55
Columbus	OH	40.00	50.00	73.50	50.00	26.50
Denver	CO	39.75	50.25	73.75	50.25	26.75
Des Moines	IA	41.53	48.47	71.97	48.47	24.97
Detroit	MI	42.42	47.58	71.08	47.58	24.08
Fargo	ND	46.90	43.10	66.60	43.10	19.60
Honolulu	HI	21.35	68.65	92.15	68.65	45.15
Houston	TX	29.97	60.03	85.53	60.03	36.53
Indianapolis	IN	39.73	50.27	73.77	50.27	26.77
Jackson	MS	32.32	57.68	81.18	57.68	34.18
Jacksonville	FL	30.33	59.67	83.17	59.67	36.17
Kansas City	MO	39.32	50.68	74.18	50.68	27.18
Las Vegas	NV	36.08	53.92	77.42	53.92	30.42
Little Rock	AR	35.22	54.78	78.28	54.78	31.28
Los Angeles	CA	33.93	56.07	79.57	56.07	32.57
Louisville	KY	38.23	51.77	75.27	51.77	28.27
Manchester	NH	42.93	47.07	70.57	47.07	23.57
Memphis	TN	35.35	54.65	78.15	54.65	31.15
Milwaukee	WI	42.95	47.05	70.55	47.05	23.55
Minneapolis	MN	44.83	45.17	68.67	45.17	21.67
New Orleans	LA	29.98	60.02	83.52	60.02	36.52

City	State	Latitude	Spring Equinox	Summer Equinox	Fall Equinox	Winter Equinox
New York City	NY	40.77	49.23	72.73	49.23	25.73
Newark	NJ	40.70	49.30	72.80	49.30	25.80
Oklahoma City	OK	35.40	54.60	78.10	54.60	31.10
Omaha	NE	41.30	48.70	72.20	48.70	25.20
Philadelphia	PA	39.88	50.12	73.62	50.12	26.62
Phoenix	AZ	33.43	56.57	80.07	56.57	33.07
Portland	ME	43.65	46.35	69.85	46.35	22.85
Portland	OR	45.60	44.40	67.90	44.40	20.90
Providence	RI	41.73	48.27	71.77	48.27	24.77
Salt Lake City	UT	40.78	49.22	72.72	49.22	25.72
Seattle	WA	47.45	42.55	66.05	42.50	19.05
Sioux Falls	SD	43.58	46.42	69.92	46.42	22.92
Virginia Beach	VA	36.82	53.18	76.68	53.18	29.68
Washington	DC	38.85	51.15	74.65	51.15	27.65
Wichita	KS	37.65	52.35	75.85	52.35	28.85
Wilmington	DE	39.67	50.33	73.83	50.23	26.83

Getting Additional Cold-Sink Sunshine

You may find that in the very northern latitudes the four foot cold-sink will still not allow enough of the sun's rays to reach the grow bed during critical times of the year. (This would probably be of most importance when you were able to supplement that meager sunshine with grow lights). But what then?

Well, there are several options. One is to have plants there in containers that you can elevate. Another is to plant that area last in early spring and with long-germinating seed so that when the seedlings finally poke through, the sun has arrived at that spot. Or you can wait and transplant seedlings themselves. But perhaps your best solution might be to put windows up top in that southernmost wall.

That would involve making an excavation in the earth to the south a workable distance out. If your project is on a hillside, you will have to displace less earth and your drainage will be easier from the excavation — you need only to pitch the excavation towards a selected drainage spot and dig a small ditch downhill there.

On flat land the project is a little more difficult. You will need to dig an actual window well. If you don't have a gutter to catch the precipitation off the glazing, and if your ground drains really well, you may get away with pitching the window-well away from the structure so that the moisture collects there while being absorbed into the earth. Otherwise you are advised to raise the height of the southern wall (now composed of windows) as mentioned earlier, and install gutters and a hose to run the water off away from the structure.

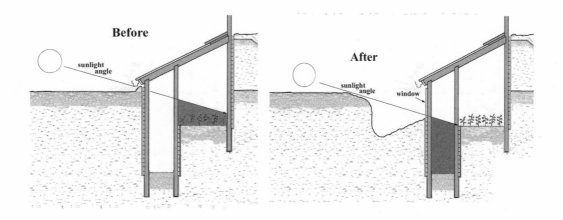

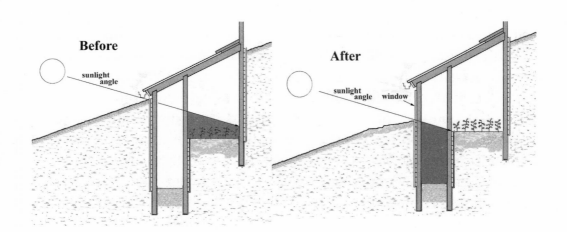

Plywood Vents

On the Garden House greenhouse we did something which may be unique. Instead of glazing everywhere on the roof, we had one section which was plywood. At first glance this seems self-defeating. You normally want just as much transparent or translucent surface above your plants as possible. But this plywood was hinged and it served as our exhaust vent. When you opened the door down at one end and the plywood vent at the other there was a great flow of hot air out.

We think this concept is valuable. Here in the northern hemisphere, it shades very little of the greenhouse growing area as long as the plywood is on the northernmost part of the roof. This is also the highest part and where you want the vent anyway. In the summertime, when it might actually shade some of the plants, is when you would open it for venting, and this allows in 100 percent of the growth rays, not 84 percent or whatever. In the cooler weather when the sun is at a lower angle the vent closed is likely to shade none of the growing area at all as you can see from the accompanying diagrams. The width of the plywood can be adjusted to make up for shortness of glazing if you make a mistake in ordering or measuring, or if your desired length is otherwise not available to you.

If you use this concept be sure to have insulation on the underside of the plywood. The insulation can also serve as a shim to bring the plywood up over the top of the glazing. Obviously, the plywood must overlap the glazing like a shingle for the water to run off properly. Raise the hinges accordingly on the back wall. Use hooks or latches for fastening to the extended north wall posts when the vent is open. All the diagrams shown, except one for Houston, are for four-foot plywood vents. Two-foot vents work well too.

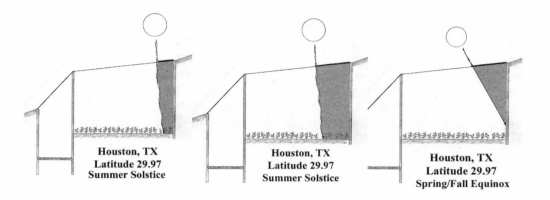

Houston, TX
Latitude 29.97
Summer Solstice

Houston, TX
Latitude 29.97
Summer Solstice

Houston, TX
Latitude 29.97
Spring/Fall Equinox

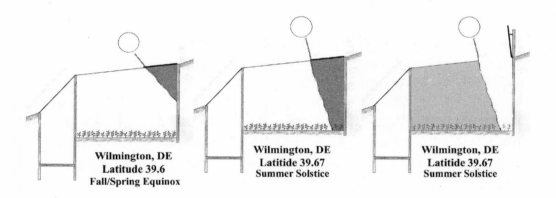

Wilmington, DE
Latitude 39.6
Fall/Spring Equinox

Wilmington, DE
Latitide 39.67
Summer Solstice

Wilmington, DE
Latitide 39.67
Summer Solstice

Canadian Border
Latitude 48.94
Summer Solstice

Canadian Border
Latitude 48.94
Spring/Fall Equinox

Canadian Border
Latitude 48.94
Summer Solstice

The question may arise as to why we don't grow in pots and trays on raised tables. It would be easier in some circumstances to reach the plants and they would be elevated up out of some of the cooler areas of the greenhouse. They would also be up out of gopher range. Why do we grow in the earth on the floor of the greenhouse?

These are good questions and they deserve reasoned answers. The first is that we do grow on raised tables. These are (or what would be) the tops of the chicken and duck/geese houses against the north wall and the surface above the heat sink water barrels. We certainly advise making use of those areas for plant production.

But we are partial to growing in Mother Earth herself rather than in containers. The roots have a great deal more freedom to stretch out as they desire. They can go as deep as they want. They often stay warmer on cold nights and winter days. A final reason, and it's a really big one, is that the earth beneath will irrigate your plants when you can't water your greenhouse because of travel or schedule conflicts. Mulch will help immeasurably in this also. I've lost many a potted plant because I was behind in just a few days watering, but have been numerous times astounded at how well the earth-bedded plants do despite weeks of watering neglect.

Oh, yeah, one more thing: Plants just seem to *do* better in the ground.

Designing for Structural Strength

Ah, a tricky subject, this. Just as we can't give you a one size greenhouse that suits all, we can't give you universal building specs either. Factors that change post, girder, and rafter dimensions include type of glazing, length of span, objects hanging from the rafters, hillside or flatland greenhouse, soil conditions and wind and snow loads.

Where you should be able to get help for this is from your local county or municipal building department. Don't want to mess with those guys? Don't blame you. However, consider this: it is reported that most places do not require building permits for small stand-alone greenhouses. Ones attached to dwellings are another matter, especially if there is an entrance directly from the house. But permit or not, don't let it throw you. The building department is there to serve, not harass you.

One good reason for dealing with them is that they have engineering backgrounds They also have a wealth of written and computer material to draw on. They can advise you on lumber dimensions based on wind and snow loads, and soil conditions. And with the exception of maybe a few high-priced architects and structural engineers, are probably the only ones in your county who can. And they should advise you for free.

On the next page is some more free advice. It is not necessarily germane to your climate and conditions, so take it for what it's worth. Your local authorities may be able to help you adapt these tables to your situation.

Engineering Report

Everything in this report assumes a post spacing of 4' east and west. All are calculated to withstand 25 pounds per square inch combined live and dead weight. *Dead* is the weight of the glazing material, the roofing structure and what might reasonably be expected to be hung from it. *Live* is accumulated snow, rain, ice weight and wind pressure. This table is calculated for the roof to withstand ten inches of ice. The lumber is #1 & #2 grade "white wood" (pine and spruce) or what will withstand 1200 psi (pounds per square inch). If you are concerned about this, ask at the lumber yard for the specs of what you are buying.

Rafter length needed of span	Rafter spacing center to center	Size
12'	2'	2"x 6"
12'	4'	2"x 8"
14'	2'	2"x 8"
14'	4'	2"x10'

Another good free source of information can be found at www.sundancesupply.com, which is a polycarbonate wholesaler, (They have a $750 minimum for their polycarbonate which is about three times the cost of glazing a 16' x 16' roof. You may need to buy elsewhere.). If that is the glazing material you decide to use, their website can be a wealth of information for you.

The system you will likely want is what Sundance Supply calls cap and trim system. Pay particular attention to the spacing of your rafters and that the structure is "square" — that your corners are all precisely 90 degrees. (The dimensions of the structure itself may likely be rectangular, but the corners are "square".) The Sundance site has lots of great info on applying polycarbonate and sealing it. **I suggest that you double the amount of screws that normally go to fasten it down. Build like a hurricane or tornado might hit your place. It might.** As I write this particular section in the last days of 2006 the west coast of Washington State is still recovering from 110-mile-an-hour winds which knocked out the electricity for one million people for a week. Two weeks after the storm, some homes and businesses still haven't got the juice back on. One can only guess what it did to structures. Hundred-mile-per-hour winds are becoming common. Being earth-sheltered, your greenhouse will do better than most, but the roof and glazing are still vulnerable since it is not earthen covered.

If you glaze with material other than polycarbonate, search the web for the manufacturers' sites, greenhouse supply companies and so forth to find info on application. If you buy from a building supply store see if they have an instruction booklet. Your library may have books that will include such info. So might bookstores and big chains like Home Depot.

HOW TO GET THE RIGHT SIZED GREENHOUSE

Find out size limitations, if any, for stand-alone greenhouses in your town. If it's smaller than you want, go ahead and build it anyway, maybe one inch smaller than permitted so if there is ever trouble you are clearly within limits and they can't make you tear it down.

Then in a year or two add another section the same size if you are brave, or another greenhouse a few feet from it if you are not. You might be able to do that repeatedly. At some point you might try filling in the spaces between making one long greenhouse. Site your first structure with the possibility of adding to either the east or west walls.

198

Chapter 17
Building plans and costs

If you are wishing an environmentally-sound green-house in some of the more posh areas of America — gated communities and such — there may be some neighborly or municipal resistance to one that looks homemade and built of recycled materials. Not everyone appreciates the Raggedy-Ann, patchwork-quilt look.

We suggest that you sound out your neighbors and authorities. If it looks like conflict, turn this book and the job over to a competent carpenter and buy new materials. If there are ordinances against animals in your community, realize that the rabbits make little sound and don't smell bad and may possibly never be discovered down in the cold-sink anyway. (You must still find a way to get them out into the cool morning or evening sun — daily, if possible.) If they are discovered, you might get away with calling them pets. If not, there are other ways of raising the CO_2 level to get its remarkable growth enhancements. Compost and certain heaters are two such ways we have discussed elsewhere in this book.

Fowl may present more of a problem in posh America. I have one piece of advice here: don't for heavens sake get a rooster. If you do your neighbors will not only likely have the bird but you, too, slaughtered, plucked, cleaned, singed, dismembered and roasted for Sunday dinner. We warned you.

Though this book is written for owner/builders, everything in here applies equally to professionals — with one caveat: some carpenters may not appreciate building with used materials since they are not standardized. A collection of sliding glass doors, for example, are likely to be of differing lengths and widths. So are piles of used lumber. For a guy used to all new, standardized material and blueprints, that can be frustrating — he has to customize. It takes longer. And that raises the labor bill.

And maybe you don't have the time or resources such as a truck to haul salvaged material. Added to possible community, neighborly and laborly resistance, this might indeed convince you to build with new materials. Though we would rather see you do otherwise, you are still building a structure which is going to cut down drastically on fuel consumption, both for the structure itself and for the energy which would have otherwise been used transporting your store-bought produce from California, Mexico or Chile. Not to mention the environmental costs of the pesticides, herbicides, fungicides, waxes, preservatives and packaging. Build with clear conscience and remember that your earth-sheltered greenhouse — at least most of it — is not going to blow away like a paper bag as will the above-ground, store-bought jobs when the hurricane or tornado velocity winds strike sometime in the not-too-distant future.

So these are several of the reasons why a person might decide to go with all new material. For this reason we have researched what it could cost you to build a typical greenhouse of ours. We will examine the costs in Idaho prices for January, 2007, for two of our typical structures. Obviously, the prices are going to vary by geography and time lapse. In all likelihood your costs will be higher, perhaps significantly so. But even with all new materials it may be less than the cost of a new, factory-built, store-bought, flimsy above-ground greenhouse. And the bottom line is it will work wonderfully better. It will be a four-season greenhouse, not a two-season one.

The first greenhouse we'll look at, the smallest of the two, is much like my original greenhouse. It is just big enough to supply one person with most of his or her salad greens or kitchen herbs or tomatoes or some combination during the season and beyond. Like the bigger greenhouse it may be extended easily from the east and west ends.

Though these diagrams should pretty much explain themselves, there are some other things you should know. At first I was going to advise building in milder climates with 4x4's for posts since I thought most of the strength needed to be vertical, or compressive, and I knew that the compressive strength of a board on end is much greater than when the pressure is against the side. But my brother-in-law, that retired classic who was the head engineer on at least one Chicago subway expansion project, objected strongly. Sure, it would handle most snow loads, he said, but you also had to deal with the lateral pressure, the lateral thrust of the earth. Claimed he knew of cases where the earth pressure moved massive bridge abutments out of place. It could push those 2x4's right into the house through the two foot of earth they were buried in. It's never happened at any of my places, I pointed out (though I have had a couple of them "hinge" when I used the pier system.) How big were the posts, he demanded. Well, I had to admit that they were often a foot or more in diameter. See, he said. Much more mass. He also objected strongly to the eight-foot spacing I was giving the posts.

Now, again, you must remember that my soil is unusual in that the angle of repose is almost vertical for a year or more. It simply does not exert much pressure. Yours might exert a lot. (If it is oozy clay, forget it. You will have to excavate out some feet and backfill with sand.) Always get local advice from the soil engineers in your area.

But for ballpark engineering here is what I've finally come up with: for the north and south walls go four foot spacing between posts. Increase the size of the posts from 4"x4" to 6"x6". If you are in somewhat troublesome earth, sink the posts deeper. A normal grocery store garbage bag is about three feet tall so you could go two and a half easily (remember you want some surplus bag left on top which is not buried.) Or you could look for some leaf bags which are longer yet.

Another thing you can do is make the hole larger and pour some concrete around the post, increasing the diameter of resistance by at least half again. As always you will want to wrap the posts in several garbage bags. Concrete is another thing reputed to rot untreated wood.

These greenhouses may be stand-alone or may be attached to a structure with a basement in cold climates. Remember, we caution against attaching a sunken greenhouse to a building with footings. In extreme conditions the sunken nature of the greenhouse might allow the cold to permeate where the earth could freeze and expand beneath the footings and buckle them.

We did pricing on 16' long 6x6's and were appalled to find that they ran up into the $70 or $80 range each. Apparently they have to be custom ordered, perhaps custom milled. A 16' 2x 6 on the other hand, we priced as low as $7.99 each. Quick math will tell you that screwing three of them together will save you approximately two-thirds the cost. The same is likely true for shorter lengths. Check around with various building supply and lumber yards for competitive quotes. A second outfit quoted us 89 cents per foot, or $14.24, nearly twice the price of the first. We didn't ask the custom 6x6 price there.

This little greenhouse shows a four-foot-wide grow bed ("wide" meaning south to north or opposed to "long" meaning east to west). Four foot is a long way to reach across. This gives you the space to put some sort of a solar collector there — brick, concrete blocks or water containers. A friend once planned to use old plastic gallon milk jugs on racks or shelving. This might work if you painted them black both to enhance the solar collection and prevent the plastic from ultraviolet degradation. Use latex paint.

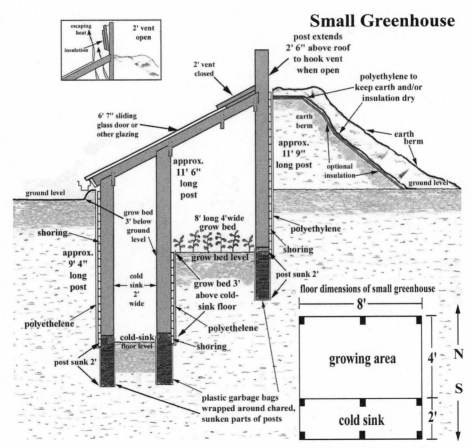

Small Greenhouse

Large Greenhouse South Half

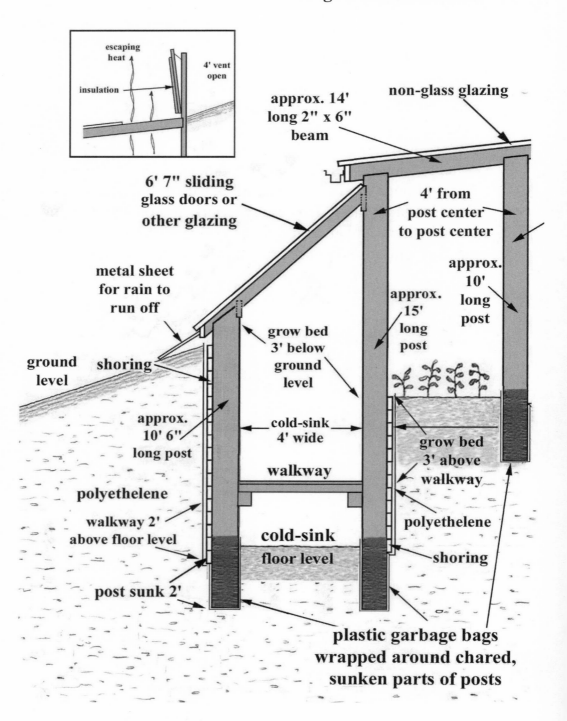

escaping
heat

insulation

4' vent
open

approx. 14'
long 2" x 6"
beam

non-glass glazing

6' 7" sliding
glass doors or
other glazing

4' from
post center
to post center

approx.
10'
long
post

metal sheet
for rain to
run off

approx.
15'
long
post

grow bed
3' below
ground
level

ground
level

shoring

approx.
10' 6"
long post

cold-sink
4' wide

grow bed
3' above
walkway

walkway

polyethelene

polyethelene

walkway 2'
above floor level

cold-sink
floor level

shoring

post sunk 2'

plastic garbage bags
wrapped around chared,
sunken parts of posts

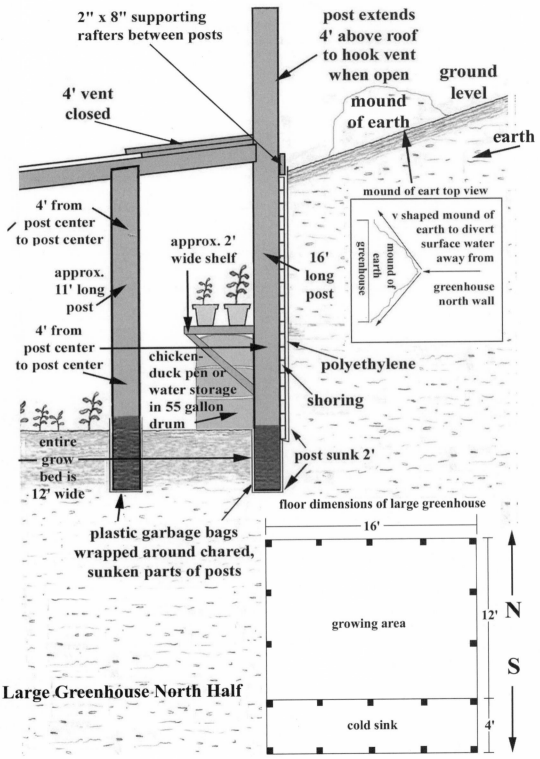

2" x 8" supporting rafters between posts

post extends 4' above roof to hook vent when open

ground level

4' vent closed

mound of earth

earth

mound of eart top view

4' from post center to post center

approx. 2' wide shelf

16' long post

v shaped mound of earth to divert surface water away from

greenhouse north wall

approx. 11' long post

4' from post center to post center

chicken-duck pen or water storage in 55 gallon drum

polyethylene

shoring

entire grow bed is 12' wide

post sunk 2'

plastic garbage bags wrapped around chared, sunken parts of posts

floor dimensions of large greenhouse

16'

growing area

12' N

S

cold sink

4'

Large Greenhouse North Half

The Earth-Sheltered Solar Greenhouse Book 205

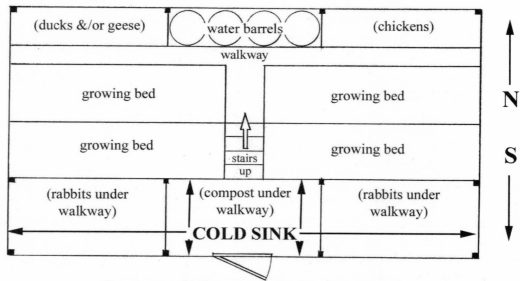

One possible greenhouse floor plan

Store-bought building material for
SMALL GREENHOUSE 8' X 6'

Lumber 2x6 T&G	$456
Vent plywood	$15
Vent hinges	$4
Vent insulation	$30
Door plywood	$15
Door knob	$10
Door hinges	$4
Door insulation	$15
(18) 12' x 2x6 post boards (making 6 posts)	$216
(9) 10' x 2x6 post boards (making 3 posts)	$90
(5) 10' x 2x6 rafters	$50
(2) 8' x 2x6 rafter supports	$16
Garbage bags	$15
Polyethylene	$20
(2) 4' x 8' polycarbonate double wall sheet glazing	$100
"H" joiner between polycarbonate sheet glazing	$7
"U" profile for edge of polycarbonate sheet glazing	$30
Stairway lumber and posts	$139
Nails and screws	$14
Gutters and supplies	$4
Total material cost for 8' x 6' small greenhouse	$1,250

Store-bought materials for
LARGE GREENHOUSE   16' x 16'

Lumber 2x 6 T&G	$1,417
(30) 16' x 2x6 post boards	$480
(27) 12' x 2x 6 post boards	$324
4'x 8' x ¾ vent plywood	$30
4'x 8' x 2 vent insulation	$15
(8) 4' x 10' polycarbonate double wall sheet glazing	$530
"H" joiner between polycarbonate sheet glazing	$57
"U" profile for polycarbonate sheet glazing edges	$102
4' x 8' x ¾ walkway plywood	$20
52' of 2x 4 for walkway	$52
(6) 8" x 2 x6 for door frame	$48
Door hinges	$4
Door knobs (locking)	$10
Door insulation	$11
Door plywood 30 x 6 x ¾	$30
(3) 16' x 2x6 rafter supports	$48
(9) 14' x 2x6 rafters	$126
Diagonal front bracing	$63
50 lb. box of nails	$50
20 lbs. of screws with gaskets	$24
4'x 8' x ¾" chicken cabinet plywood	$30
3' high chicken wire	$10
1 quart of varnish	$12
Cabinet door runners	$10
30' of 2x6 for stair steps (not T&G)	$30
(2) 8' x 8x2 for stair diagonal framing	$16
(1) 8' x 2x6 for stairway	$8
Garbage bags	$30
Polyethylene	$40
Gutters and supplies	$8
Total material cost for 16' x 16' large greenhouse	$3,635

SMALL GREENHOUSE 8' X 6' ADDITION

6 posts	$204
Lumber 2x6 T&G	$307
(2) 8' x 2x6 rafter supports	$16
(3) 10' x 2x6 rafters	$30
(2) 4' x 8' polycarbonate double wall glazing	100
"H" joiner between polycarbonate sheets	$14
"U" profile for edge of polycarbonate sheets	$15
Garbage bags	$10
Polyethylene	$14
Nails and screws	$12
Vent plywood	$15
Vent hinges	$48
Vent insulation	$4
Gutters and supplies	$4
Total material cost for 8' x 6' small greenhouse addition	$793
Small greenhouse 6' x 8'	$1,250
Small greenhouse 6' x 16'	$2,043
Small greenhouse 6' x 24'	$2,836

The eight-foot addition to each greenhouse is considerably less expensive than the costs of the eight-foot basic structure as diagramed. This is because the basic structure has two end walls which need not be factored into the addition. Even if the addition is made after the original is completed, the materials from the end wall that must be removed can and should be salvaged to make the new end wall.

Incidentally, the cost of each greenhouse presented here is somewhat higher that the real January, 2007, prices. This is because we factored all 2x6 lumber, whether plain or tongue and groove, at $1.00 per linear foot, considerably above the true market price. This is to make it easier for you to get some idea of the cost of building in 2008 or 2011, or whenever. Simply call a lumber yard and get your current price for the 2x6's and add or subtract accordingly. If the price is $1.25 per linear foot, for example, the six posts above ,which took 204 board feet to construct, would then cost $255.

LARGE GREENHOUSE 8' X16' ADDITION

(12) 16' x 2x6 post boards	$192
(6) 12' x 2x6 post boards	$72
Lumber 2x6 T&G lumber	$442
(2) 14' x 2x6 rafter boards	$28
(2) 8' x 2x6	$16
16' x 2x6 rafter support board	$16
Plywood for vent	$15
Insulation for vent	$8
Hinges for vent	$6
(4) 4' x 10' polycarbonate double wall sheet glazing	$265
"H" joiner between polycarbonate sheets	$38
"U" profile for edge of polycarbonate sheets	$32
Walkway lumber	$26
Nails/screws	$32
Gutter and supplies	$4
4'x 8' x ¾" chicken cabinet plywood	$15
3' high chicken wire	$5
Varnish	$6
Polyethylene	$20
Garbage bags	$8
Total material cost for 8' x 16' large greenhouse addition	$1,246
Large greenhouse 16' x 16'	$3,635
Large greenhouse 16' x 32'	$6,127
Large greenhouse 16' x 48'	$8,619

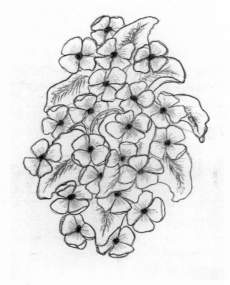

Chapter 18
Random notes

We have pretty much been giving dimensions in two foot increments in this book, at least for horizontal dimensions. Most carpenters and many designers think this way because this is how lumber is commonly sold: 8', 10', 12', 14' and 16'. With lumber prices as they are, it hurts a man to have to cut a foot off each 14' board to make a 13' wall. An 8' high wall would cost a guy 20 linear feet of lumber. Four such walls would mean a loss of 80 linear feet. If that were two-inch lumber, it would be 160 board feet.

This doesn't always apply in the shorter spaces, however. If you wanted a three-foot-wide cold-sink rather than either 2' or 4', you wouldn't have to lose two board feet by cutting two three footers out of an eight footer or one foot loss with three three footers out of a 10'. You could get four three-footers out of a 12'. Obvious as daylight, of course. Funny, though, how you can miss such things when you have 10,000 other considerations weighing on your mind — especially when you try such a building job for the first time.

You do know the true dimensions of a 2x4 is really 1½x3½? And that when the tongue is in the groove on a 2x6 T&G it measures out to 1½x5?

If you use used sliding glass doors, one way of fastening them to the rafters could be by screwing through their metal framing with long roofing screws with waterproof gaskets. Be sure, however, that you don't nick the glass.

We suspect (but have no evidence for whatsoever) that when your plants stop growing in the fall because the days get shorter (phototropic reaction) that some bright lights shining in the greenhouse for four or five hours per night might encourage them to keep growing or at least maturing. We suspect that this will work with plain old incandescent bulbs, not just the grow lights. This assumes that there is still enough sunshine for photosynthesis. This supposition is based on the widespread rural knowledge that, if they are also kept warm, chickens will lay eggs much better in the winter if their coop is illuminated for part of the night.

> A friend told me in 1978 of an earth-sheltered greenhouse built in Massachusetts without a cold-sink. The owner, recognizing the problem of cold air settling on the plants, installed a fan to keep it moving, to mix it up. This approach is certainly better than none. It's the same principal as the horizontally rotating fans people install in their homes to blow the warm air down from cathedral ceilings. But it consumes fossil fuels, is costly, is subject to disruptions and doesn't warm the air. The cold-sink solves all of these.

Oh, almost forgot: what is the Wrigley's chewing gum defense? That's when you put sticks of unwrapped Juicy Fruit gum in the gopher burrows. They are supposed to eat it and get all plugged up and leave or die, or something. Don't know. Didn't work for me. Maybe I was supposed to chew it a bit first, but it hasn't done any better than the electronic sound or vibration devices I've tried. All Wrigley's has ever done for my gophers is give them brilliant white teeth and kissable breath.

Postmortem

So how have my earth-sheltered greenhouses held up over the years? The original one, the one where the cold-sink was invented, was cannibalized by (incorporated into) the garden house after a few years of fairly successful operation. Only "fairly successful" because, as you will recall, it was in the shade of a tall ridge to the south and received almost no direct sunlight after October. Nevertheless it would carry tomatoes into November and kale and other hardies into or through January.

The Garden House itself, alas, finally met its demise in 2006. It had had a bad leak in the roof from the start (deadly to wooden structures) which I never got around to repairing due to the press of other projects. Anything I don't live in or use constantly myself gets short shift, for the experiments and projects are many on my land. Except for its minuscule size, though, it was a fine house and is missed.

And the hillside greenhouse? Ah, another case of benign neglect. Arthritis in both knees, wrists and thumbs have kept this guy from using it much in recent years, and the carpenter ants have been at it. Nevertheless it stands, and the Fairall family sharing the land have made inquiries about using it in 2007. We'll keep you posted.

The original PSP underground house, built in 1971 and expanded in 1975, is doing just fine, thank you. It withstood the 13 to 18 foot of snows the winter of '97 when trailers, Quonset huts, a school gymnasium and automobile roofs were collapsing under the loads. It has a couple of leaks in the roof but they only show up usually at spring breakup and not always then.

A 1972 trailer on my land, by way of comparison, despite a second installed roof, a "snow roof", leaks from at least twenty places under a snow load. Since my house cost $500 and has served well for 35 years, we can probably call it an unquestioned success. That comes out to roughly $14.30 per year for a snug, beam-ceilinged, 370 square foot house.

214

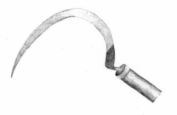

CHAPTER 19
**A final word about gophers
(Which you may not believe
but which I swear is the absolute truth)**

This happened at the 1982 National Rainbow Gathering in eastern Washington State, my first National. I had been at several functions where there was a Rainbow presence – barter fairs, healing gatherings, the Black Hills Survival Gathering in 1980 – so I knew well the legends of the mystical-magical things which often happen at Rainbow Gatherings. But I wasn't quite prepared for a mystical gopher.

It is in the spirit of the Rainbows as well as the hippies (the same folks, some would say) to serve others, to give. So at Rainbow Gatherings almost everything is free – free food from the free kitchens, free spiritual teachings, free massages, free sweat lodges, free showers, free drumming, free music and dancing. Free other things, too. If you are in the spirit you find something you can share. Mine was expertise on underground housing. I'd been living underground for eleven years, teaching it for ten and had published a book on the subject four years earlier. The gathering was in my neck of the woods, so many recognized me by sight, told their acquaintances, and I found I was spending much of my time talking about the same stuff over and over again. No fun. So I decided to give a class on underground design.

I put up signs, made an announcement at the main circle, and the next day was teaching on a sandy knoll overlooking the First Church of Venal Love (never mind about that.) I was kneeling, sitting back on my heels, barefoot as always, and had maybe a dozen people around me – nine sitting in front and three standing behind peering down over my shoulders as I dug in the soft earth, modeling underground structures. I was explaining why a person should never build a dreaded "First Thought House" – an underground house tunneled into a hillside with a big blast of windows only on the downhill side. It is the most common design in underground housing and is a disaster. It is why underground housing has never taken off as it should. There is no balance of light in the rooms that have windows, no cross ventilation. Some rooms have no windows at all. Plus the moisture that lands on the roof drains back and is joined by the rain coming down the hillside, and eventually that back wall is going to leak.

"And most of those first thought houses have a door on only one side," I explained. "You can be trapped in a place like that. It could be fire, cave in, bears, angry loggers or the sheriff. Whatever. I don't know of a single other animal that lives underground that has entrances on only one side. As far as I'm concerned, this means that the other animals are smarter than humans."

A moment later I felt something furry against my ankle. I was concentrating on my talk, so I only absentmindedly reached back to brush off what I assumed was a caterpillar. But it was much larger than a caterpillar! I jerked my head down just in time to see a pocket gopher dive back into its hole four feet away. I was astonished. I looked up at the three guys standing behind me who now had huge jack-o'-lantern grins on their faces.

"What was that all about?" I asked.

"The moment you said that about the animals being smarter than the humans that … animal … popped up from its hole, ran over to you and began rubbing its head on your ankle," one of the guys said, making caressing motions with his head. The other two guys still grinning, confirmed it with nods and grunts of affirmation.

I was stunned. It took me a moment to recover. All I could say was, "Uh … well … ummm … Only at a Rainbow Gathering!"

Never underestimate a gopher.

Gopher

Index

acrylics 64,66
Aluminized Mylar 72, 75
aluminum foil 58
America, consumption records 15
angles of repose 54-55, 202
ants 94, 96-97
aquaculture 122-23
attached greenhouses 149, 151-152
"automatic arm" openers 81
backfilling 43, 46, 90, 142
bone meal 97-98
"bone support" 48-50
boric acid 98
Brassica plants 131-132
Bubel, Mike & Nancy 137, 143, 145-146
carbon dioxide, and green houses 116-120
cardboard, as insulation 74
cayenne red pepper 98
charring/garbage bag post system 45-46
chickens in greenhouses 121-122, 200
chimney effect 80
cold-sink 14, 36,37, 40, 50, 54, 55, 76, 84, 90, 112, 114, 151-152, 173, 177, 179-180, 182, 199
Coleman, Eliot 120-121

collapsing of walls 54
convection currents 79, 152
cost analysis
    small 8' x 6' 206
    large 16' x 16' 207
    small addition 208
    large addition 209
Cornell University 106
Cranshaw, Whitney 106
creosote post method 45
crownvetch 77
counteracting pressure 48-50
De Korne, James B. 116, 118-119, 123
digging by hand 54-55
DSB (double-strength B glass) 60
double-wall glazing 66
double-wall polycarbonate 68
duck breeds 120
ducks in greenhouse 120-121
Earth-Sheltered Houses 53
east/west axis 84
EPDM 44
fans 81, 107
far-infrared radiation 72
fiberglass 64-65
    combustibility of 65
FRP (fiberglass-reinforced polyester 64
$500 underground house 44, 101

$50 & Up Underground House Book   43, 80

$50 underground house   43, 44, 80, 141

fifty-five gallon barrels and drums   85-86

Filon   65, 174

Findhorn Community   25

Foamglass   74

foam insulating panels   74-76

Four Season Harvest   120

fowl in greenhouses   118-122

fungus gnat adult   106

Garden Insects of North America   106

geese in greenhouses   119-20

Gibbons, Ewell   18

glass for glazing   59-63

glazing   33, 57-68, 175, 181

   pitch of   33, 34,180-182

gophers   27, 28, 30, 33, 34, 94-95, 96, 98-102, 107, 137-141, 183

gopher traps   138-139

grasshoppers   94-95

greenhouse layouts   203-205

Growing Food in Solar Greenhouses   112

growing in pots and trays   194

growing seasons

   choices of   172

   for various crops   180

   North America   13

   North Idaho   17

harvest, North America   13

heat-sink   37, 58, 77, 84, 177

heat units measuring system   23

conventional greenhouses vs. underground   37-40

High-R Sheathing   72

hillside creep   50

hillside greenhouse costs   174

hinging   44-45

hoop and plastic system   23, 24-25

humidistat   128-29

humidity   128-29, 143

Hunger Signs in Crops   117

Hydroponic Hot House, The: Low-cost, High-yield Greenhouse Gardening   116

Idaho, north   15, 17, 19, 161

"Insect Management in Green houses"   102

insect traps   104-05

Integrated Pest Management Program (UC)   106

International Monetary Fund   14

irrigation   177-78

Johnson, Denis   161

K-value   72

lacewings   104

ladybugs (ladybird beetles)   103

lateral thrust   201

mastic glazing compound   62

mice   94, 98

milled lumber   45, 46, 51

mirrors   58
mites   102-03
moles and voles   137
Mother Earth News   61
mulch   92, 137
Naples General Store   62
National Fertilizer Assoc.   117
Natural Resources
    Conservation Service   55
Nearing, Scott and Helen   59
nematodes   103
New Alchemy Institute   123
new vs. recycled materials
                                      199-200
non-passive solar heating   84
northern latitudes,
    greenhouse design   172-173
north/south axis   50
nutrients for soil   130-131
organic gardening   18-19
*Organic Gardening and
    Farming Magazine*   123
organic sprays   104
OSHA   55
passive solar collection   84
Pavlovian training   121-122
pest specimens   107
petroleum-based plastics   64
pH factors   107, 130
pier post method   44-45
pitch, of glazing 33,180-81,189
    of sun   35
pit greenhouse   116
plastic glazes   62

polycarbonates   64, 67
    for glazing   196
polyethylene
    for glazing   57
    for greenhouse covers   58-59
polyisocyanurate   71-72
polystyrene   71-72, 73
polyurethane   71-72
post and beam construction   44
PSP posts, setting   47
    structural support   179-180
PSP method   14-15, 43-48,
                       122,178-80, 202
power blackouts   136, 153
praying mantis   103
"Protect Your Garden with
    Beneficial Bugs"   106
putty   62
putty gun   62-63
Quonset huts   73
rabbits
    breeding   115
    effects of underground
        housing on   115
    hutches   113
    neighbors' reactions to   199
rafters   44, 47, 48, 51, 52, 53,
           61, 71, 76, 128, 156
Rainbow Gathering
                   160-162, 215-217
rain gutters, for water
    collection   177-78
Reagan administration   15

R-values (resistance values) 71-72, 74

Resources Guide for Organic Insect and Disease Management 106

rigid foam insulating panels 72-76

rigid plastics for glazing 63-68

Roy, Rob 53

Rodale's 53, 123

Ronniger, David 89

Ronniger's Seed Potatoes 89

root crops 17

Saxton, Michael 117-118

screening vents 107

secret panel 151

shading effects 129-30

shoring up
    grow hole 34
    excavations 54-55
    root cellars 142

single sheet glazing 65-66

SSB (single-strength B glass) 60

soft plastic glazing 57

solar collectors 203

storm windows 21, 59

strawberry leaf tea 18

sun angles
    for various latitudes and solstices 183-89
    winter-summer solstices 176

sustainable agriculture 14

tamping 46-48

tempered glass 60-61, 63

Territorial Seed Company 103

Thermax 72

thermometers 127-28, 129

University of California 106

University of Tennessee Agricultural Extension Service 102, 104

ventilation 79-80, 142, 173-174
    plywood 192-93

white flies 94, 104

white paint 58

Whole Earth Catalogs 81

wind scrubbing 22, 37, 39-40

windows, east-west 173-74

wire glass 61

wisegeek.com 66

Wolfe, Delores 112

World Bank 14

World Trade Organization 14

Wrigley's Chewing Gum defense 99, 138, 212

yearly mean temperature 84, 188-189

Y2K 65, 100

Bibliography

Bubel, Mike and Nancy. *Root Cellaring.* North Adams, MA: Storey Publishing, 1991.

Coleman, Eliot. *Four-Season Harvest.* White River Junction, Vermont: Chelsea Green Publishing Company, 1992, 1999.

DeKorne, James. *The Hyrdoponic Hot House: Low-Cost, High-Yield Greenhouse Gardening.* Loompanics Unlimited, 1992.

Oehler, Mike. *The $50 & Up Underground House Book.* Bonners Ferry, Idaho: Mole Publishing Company, 1978, 1979, 1981, 1992, 1997.

————— . *The Low-Cost Underground House Workshop and Survival Shelter Seminar* DVD set and Workbook. Bonners Ferry, Idaho: Mole Publishing Company, 1996.

Proulx, E. A. "Make Your Own Insulated Window Shutters Garden Way Bulletin A-80". Charlotte, Vermont: Garden Way Publishing, 1981.

Riotte, Louise. *Carrots Love Tomatoes.* Pownal, Vermont: Storey Communications, 1975, 1998.

Roy, Rob. *Earth-Sheltered Houses: How to Build an Affordable Underground House.* Gabriola Island, British Columbia, Canada: New Society Publisher's, 2006.

Suc, Nguyen Quang, Dinh Van Binh, Le Thi thu Ha and T. R. Preston. *"Effect of housing system (cage versus underground shelter) on performance of rabbits on farms,"* *Livestock Research for Rural Development,* Volume 8, Number 8, November 1996. Ho Chi Minh City, Vietnam: Finca Ecologica, University of Agriculture and Forestry, 1996. http://www.cipav.org.co/cipav/resrch/livestk/ index.htm

Twitchell, Mary. *Choosing Solar Glazes, Garden Way Bulletin A-83* . Charlotte, Vermont: Garden Way Publishing, 1981.

Wolfe, Delores. *Growing Food in Solar Greenhouses.* New York, NY: Sun Words Book, Dolphin Books, Double day & Company, Inc., 1981.

Resources

Greenhouse/Glazing Supplies

Charley's Greenhouse & Garden
Mount Vernon, WA
1-800-322-4707
www.charleysgreenhouse.com

International Greenhouse Company
Georgetown, IL
1-888-281-9337
www.greenhousemegastore.com

Gothic and Grenhouses, Inc.
Mobile, AL
1-800-531-4769
www.gothicarchgreenhouses.com

Sundance Supply
Olga, WA
www.sundancesupply.com

The Greenhouse Catalog
Salem, OR
1-800-825-1925
www.greenhousecatalog.com

Biological Insect Control

Charley's Greenhouse & Garden
Mount Vernon, WA
1-800-233-2615
www.charleysgreenhouse.com

Gaiam Real Goods
Hopland, CA 95449
1-707-744-2100
www.realgoods.com

Park's Seeds
Greenwood, SC
1-800-845-3369
www.parkseed.com

Shumway's, R. H
Randolph, WI
1-800-342-9461
www.rhshumway.com

Subsistence Farming Information

Primal Seeds
www.primalseeds.org/index.htm

Seeds

Abundant Life Seeds
open pollinated, organic
Saginaw, OR
ww.abundantlifeseeds.com

Azure Standard- organic
   Western USA regional
      deliveries only
   Dufur, OR
   1-541-467-2230
   www.azurestandard.com

Bountiful Gardens
   open pollinated, organic
   Willits, CA
   1-707-459-6410
   www.bountifulgardens.org

Bulkfoods.com
   Toledo, OH
   1-888-285-5266
   www.bulkfoods.com

Burgess Seed & Plant Co.
   Bloomington, IL
   1-309-662-7761
   www.eburgess.com

W. Atlee Burpee & Co
   Warminster, PA
   1-800-888-1447
   www.burpee.com

Farmer Seed & Nursery
   Division of Plantron, Inc.
   Faribault, MN
   1-507-334-1623
   www.farmerseed.com

Gardensgreen
   Auburn, GA
   1-770-867-0426
   www.gardensgreen.com

Gurney's Seed & Nursery
   Greendale, IN
   1-513-354-1491
   www.gurneys.com

Henry Fields Seed &
   Nursery Co.
   Aurora, IN
   1-513-354-1494
   www.henryfields.com

Johnny's Selected Seeds
   heirloom, organic
   Winslow, Maine
   1-877-564-6697
   www.johnnyseeds.com

Mountain Valley Growers
   organic
   Squaw Valley, CA
   1-559-338-2775
   www.mountainvally
   growers.com

Nichols Garden Nursery-
   Albany, OR
   open-pollinated
   1-800-422-3985
   www.nicholsgarden
   nursery.com

Main Street Seed and
   Supply Co
   Bay City, Michigan
   1-989-893-3577 local
   1-866-229-3276 toll free
   www.mainstreetseedan
   supply.com

Park's Seeds
  Greenwood, SC
  1-800-845-3369
  www.parkseed.com

Peaceful Valley Farm &
  Garden Supply
  open pollinated, organic
  Grass Valley, CA
  1-888-784-1722
  www.GrowOrganic.com

Pleasant Hill Grain
  Aurora, NE
  1-800-321-1073
  ww.pleasanthillgrain.com

Redwood City Seed Co.
  open pollinated, organic
  Redwood City, CA
  1-650-325-7333
  www.batnet.com/rwc-seed/

Roguelands Vegetable Seeds
  www.vegetableseed.net/
  index.html
  heirloom
  c/o Anioleka Seed
  Company-US division
  Grants Pass, OR
    or
  c/o Anioleka Seeds Co.-
  Intl. division
  Portlethen, Aberdeenshire
  Scotland

Sand Mountain Herbs
  Fyffe, AL
  www.sandmountainherbs.
  com

Seed Savers Exchange
  Decorah, IA
  heirloom, organic
  1-563-382-5990
  www.seedsaves.org

Seeds of Change
  organic
  Santa Fe NM
  1-888-762-7333
  www.seedsofchange.com

Shumway's, R. H
  Randolph, WI
  1-800-342-9461
  www.rhshumway.com

Southern Exposure Seed
  Exchange
  heirloom, organic,
  open pollinated
  Mineral, VA
  1-540-894-9481
  ww.southernexposure.com

Sow Organic Seed Co
  organic
  Williams, OR
  1-888-709-7333
  www.organicseed.com

Stokes Seeds, Inc
  Buffalo, NY
  1-800-396-9238
  www.stokeseeds.com

Territorial Seed Company
  open pollinated, organic
  Cottage Grove, OR
  1-800-626-0866
  www.territorial-seed.com/
  stores/1/index.cfm

The Thyme Garden Herb
  Company
  open pollinated, organic
  Alsea, OR
  1-541-487-8671
  www.thymegarden.com

Tomato Growers Supply
  Fort Myers, FL
  1-888-478-7333
  www.tomatogrowers.com

Totally Tomatoes
  Randolph, WI
  1-888-477-7333
  www.totallytomato.com

Treehelp.com
  USA
  Buffalo, NY
  1-877-356-7333

  Canada
  Toronto, ON
  www.treehelp.com

Victory Seed Company
  open pollinated
  Molalla, OR
  1-503-829-3126
  www.victoryseeds.com

Walton Feed, Inc.
  Montpelier, ID
  1-800-847-0465
  www.watlonfeed.com

Wood Prairie Farm
  Bridgewater, ME
  1-800-829-9765
  www.woodprairie.com/
  catalog/index.html

Tools & Supplies

Azure Standard- (see listing
under seeds)
Bailey's
  (Home Office)
  Laytonville, CA
  1-800-322-4539
  www.baileys-online.com
    or
  (Southeastern Division)
  Jackson, TN
  1-731-422-1300

Betterbee, Inc
  Greenwich, NY
  1-800-632-3379
  www.betterbee.com

Harbor Freight Tools
Camarillo, CA
1-800-423-2567
www.harborfreight.com

Lehman's
Dalton, OH
USA
1-877-438-5346

International
1-330-828-8828
www.lehmans.com

Pleasant Hill Grain
Aurora, NE
1-800-321-1073
ww.pleasanthillgrain.com

Walton Feed, Inc.
Montpelier, ID
1-800-847-0465
www.watlonfeed.com

We recently were handed a catalog from Peaceful Valley Farm and Garden Supply (page 226) an outfit I had been unaware of before. I was deeply impressed. The catalog is so comprehensive about organic farming and gardening that I could have done much of the research for this book about pests, beneficial insects organic sprays, soil conditions and a great deal more from its pages. I checked with one of the top organic growers in our county, and she reports them to be very reputable. Highly recommended.

Ordering Information

If you appreciated his book, you may be ready for more of Mike Oehler's works. Those exploring the concept of earth-sheltered housing will find *The $50 & Up Underground House Book* a revelation. In its sixteenth printing, seventh edition, with more than 116,000 copies sold, it is the classic in its field. It has received more than 45 rave reviews. National Public Radio's Daniel Lusk called it "A wonderfully unsophisticated manual … a valuable document." *Earth Shelter Living Magazine* called it, "By far the best example of low-cost earth sheltering we've found", and the Chicago Sun Times said, "Oehler is definitely on to something."

But you need windows in an underground house, lots of them.

This is where most people, including professional architects, fail miserably. It is why underground housing has not become the raging success it deserves to be. Let the master take you through the same course he has taught across North America and Europe, frequently under the sponsorship of university architecture departments. It is all contained in his six-hour three DVD set, *The Underground House Workshop and Survival Shelter Seminar.* It comes complete with a workbook, design kit and shelter plans. To our knowledge, nothing else, anywhere, comes even remotely close to the wealth of information contained here. Not only do you learn the thirteen methods of design to get windows, sunshine and views underground (and why you shouldn't use the "foolish four" favored by most professional architects) but you will learn how to build a low-cost, effective family shelter. And you will take video tours of both Irvin-Ebenezer's Garden House and the Hillside Greenhouse featured in this present volume.

ORDER NOW with credit card from: **1-800-328-8790**
or online at **www.undergroundhousing.com**
or with check/money order address below

Please send:

_____ Copies of **The $50 & Up Underground House Book** @ $19.95 _____
_____ Six-hour, three DVD combined **Workshop Seminar** sets @ $95 _____
_____ **The Earth-Sheltered Solar Greenhouse Book** .... $24.95 _____
_____ **Hippy Survival Guide** (written by Oehler for Y2K but
            applicable to today) .... $14..95 _____
_____ **One Mexican Sunday** (Oehler's literary classic) ....$17 _____
Add $4.50 postage and handling for DVD's, $3 for books ($1
   each additional book) .... _____

NAME _____   Total enclosed _____
ADDRESS _____
CITY _____ STATE _____ ZIP _____

**SEND TO: MOLE PUBLISHING CO., 333 GANDHI WAY,
BONNERS FERRY, ID 83805**

About the Author

Mike Oehler has been designing, building and living underground since 1971 on his North Idaho 46 acre homestead. He has been gardening in his unique earth-sheltered greenhouses since 1976. Author of *The $50 &*

Up Underground House Book, his work has received international acclaim and resulted in his lecturing or conducting workshops in Canada, England, Scotland, Belgium, the Netherlands, Germany and 26 American states, frequently under the sponsorship of university architecture departments. More of his work maybe viewed at www.undergroundhousing.com.